Ch_____

Hugh Piggott

© Hugh Piggott, 2006
The Centre for Alternative Technology,
Machynlleth, Powys,
SY20 9AZ, Wales
Tel. 01654 705950
Fax. 01654 702782
email: pubs@cat.org.uk
Website: www.cat.org.uk/catpubs
www.ecobooks.co.uk

ISBN 1-90217-531-X

Photographs: Hugh Piggott unless credited
Illustrations: Hugh Piggott, Graham Preston

Printed on 100% recycled paper by
Cambrian Printers 01970 627111

The details in this book are provided in good faith and believed
correct at the time of writing. However, no responsibility is taken for
any errors. Our publications are updated regularly; please let us know
of any amendments or additions which you think may be useful for
future editions.

Contents

Introduction

Wind energy is an environmentally friendly power source and perhaps the most conspicuous of the renewable sources of energy. It's green and it's fun, and people want to get involved. Why not put a windmill on the roof and run the house off it? Well, unfortunately it may not be that simple.

A Marlec FM1803 wind turbine at CAT.

The wind

Wind is a free source of energy that has been used for thousands of years. The main advantages of wind energy are that it is both abundant and clean. There are no fuel costs, nor are there any emissions of CO_2 or other pollutants.

The disadvantages of wind energy are that it is diffuse and intermittent. Hydro turbines, diesel engines and most other prime movers can be made quite compact, but wind turbines have to be built large enough to process large amounts of air. Most people have an exaggerated idea of the power available per square metre of wind.

Wind is also quite random in its behaviour over time – blowing hard one day and flat calm another. The changes are dramatic and hard to predict. Most people do not fully realise that wind turbines only produce power when the wind blows hard enough, and that the amount of power is constantly changing.

A doubling of windspeed results in an eightfold increase in available power. Light winds carry hardly any power at all, so that windmills become useless. Strong winds carry far too much power, threatening the windmill with destruction. The power you actually get has much more to do with the wind, than the windmill.

Being dependent on the wind, windmills are apt to give you plenty of power at times when you do not need it, and none when you do. Matching supply to demand is more complicated than it would be with an engine driven generator, for example. Where wind is the only supply, then you need a battery to store the energy for calm periods. The wind turbine is actually part of a whole system tailored to provide a power supply.

Types of wind system

There are three main types of system in which small wind turbines are used. The same make of wind turbine can often be used for any of these purposes, but there will be slight differences in the design for each.

Stand-alone power systems

Small wind systems can successfully supply electrical power in circumstances where the mains electricity grid is not available and there is plenty of wind. Batteries are needed to provide power when the wind is insufficient and to absorb power when there is too much wind. But if you are already grid connected, then it makes more sense to use the grid as an energy bank, rather than batteries.

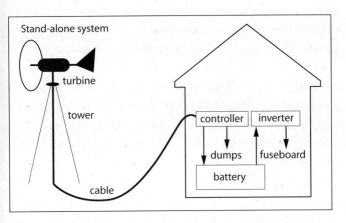

Grid-connected systems

Wind energy can also work well as part of the national grid supply. It is more cost-effective to use very large turbines in wind-farms than it is small wind turbines. Just as it is more

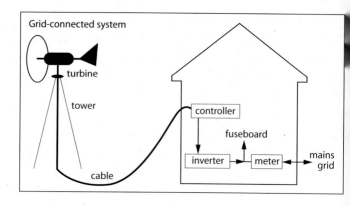

Grid-connected system

turbine

tower

controller

fuseboard

inverter → meter → mains grid

cable

cost effective to deliver goods in big lorries rather than on motorbikes, there are economies of scale. Despite this fact, we are now seeing a huge increase in the use of small wind systems by grid-connected users.

The electricity produced by the turbine will be directly used in the house if there is sufficient demand, thus saving on electricity bills. Any surplus is exported to the grid, and any shortfall is imported from the grid on a moment-by-moment basis.

Grid-connected systems are cheaper and more efficient than stand alone systems. But they will shut down when there is a power cut on the grid. A small wind turbine cannot sustain a stable output without a battery or a grid connection to smooth out the fluctuations in supply and demand.

It is technically possible to connect a battery-based system to the grid, but the equipment to do this is not permitted in the UK. (All inverters connected to the grid must carry a current Engineering Recommendation G83/1 Type Test Certificate in order to satisfy the District Network Operator [DNO].) In any case there are strong economic reasons to avoid batteries. Battery technology is not environmentally friendly either, so overall it is better not to use them unless they are really needed. A back-up generator could actually be more environmentally friendly, unless power cuts are frequent.

Heating systems

The third, and least common option is to use wind energy directly to heat your home. This type of system is the cheapest of all and operates independently of batteries or the grid. The drawback is that it does not provide usable electricity for other purposes. Heat energy has a much lower value than electrical energy.

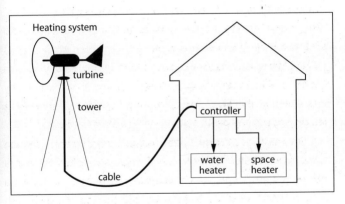

Electricity is the most expensive and inefficient way to heat a home. Electrical energy is of a higher grade than heat energy, in so far as three times as much fuel is used in a power station to produce electrical energy compared with the fuel used in a boiler to produce the same amount of heat energy directly. Conversely, you could produce three times as much heat from a given amount of electricity using a 'geothermal' heat pump where there is one installed. So it is more efficient to use a wind turbine to produce electricity and to then install a heat pump for heating purposes.

How to use this book

This booklet is about choosing equipment for small, wind systems. It will help you find out what you need, or indeed whether windpower is the best solution for you.

Section 1: Small wind turbine electrics…explains the electrical ins and outs of living with wind energy systems. Here we look at the various parts that make up a windpower system – there is more than just a wind turbine involved.

Section 2: Assessing your needs…helps you find out how much energy you actually use. This is vital when designing a stand-alone system. And it can help you to trim your electricity use down to match the available wind energy. It is often more cost effective to spend money on more efficient appliances than to buy a bigger wind turbine.

Section 3: Siting small wind turbines…takes a hard look at the site and at how to make an informed guess at the amount of energy available from the wind. This is where you find out that an urban rooftop is the least suitable site for a windpower system.

Section 4: Understanding wind turbine specifications… gets into the nitty gritty of windy jargon: rated power and rotor diameter, etc. This should allow you to discuss your needs with the experts. This is the section about wind turbines as machines.

The conclusion…pulls all the threads together and helps you make a decision. What is the logical process for designing a system, and who ever follows it?

Appendix 1… is a glossary of terms.

Appendix 2… is a market survey listing all the small wind turbines we can find on the UK market today.

Appendix 3… gives useful equations.

Appendix 4… lists some useful web links.

Economics

Wind energy is free. Why, then, are there so few wind turbines to be seen cashing in on this? The answer is that the wind is a diffuse and fickle source of energy, and the equipment needed to convert it into usable power is expensive. Small wind turbines only make sense in windy locations, (see Section 3: Siting small wind turbines), and even then it will take years before the energy produced repays the initial cost.

At present, the cheapest wind-generated electricity comes from windfarms, using turbines about 60 metres tall, feeding power straight into the national grid. This costs around 3 pence per kilowatt-hour (kWh) – cheaper than coal or nuclear energy if you include the near incalculable cost of cleaning up after these conventional sources.

This book is concerned with small wind turbines, which are expensive to buy and install per kWh of electricity produced, compared to the windfarm monsters. To meet the electricity consumption of the average UK home you would need plenty of wind, and a turbine with rotor-blades about 2-3 metres long (about 5 metres 'diameter'). The windmill alone would cost over

£5,000 and the total system would probably cost over £15,00
Electricity production could be about 5-10,000 kWh units p
year, with a value of about £300-1,000 (depending on windspee
and tariffs).

The paperwork for connecting small windmills to the gr
is rather complicated in this country, but it is getting easie
Network operators will require the inverter to comply with
technical standard, either G83 for small systems, or G59 if th
current exceeds 16 amps (representing 3-4 kW). Then you w
have to find a good tariff agreement with a supplier. (Tariff is th
price per kWh unit sold.)

Suppliers offer packages with tariffs for each unit the
provide (import), and tariffs for any units you sell back to ther
(export). You can also be paid extra for all the units you produc
(whether you then use them or sell them) through a schem
called Renewable Obligation Certificates (ROCs). At present, th
rate for ROCs is 3-4 pence per kWh unit. Export tariffs are almos
the same as the import tariff for what you use now (often aroune
7 pence) in some of the latest deals. Things are improving fas
Even so the payback on a domestic wind system will probabl
be several years, and your money could produce more gree
electricity if invested in a large wind project, or used to buy wind
generated electricity from a windfarm.

Remote sites are another matter. Off-grid household powe
consumption can be slashed by using low-energy light bulbs
and avoiding the use of electric heaters (except in high winds
when there is surplus power). Stand-alone wind systems car
be cost effective when set against the cost of diesel generatec
electricity for example, and a 3-4 metre diameter windmill car

rovide 24-hour power to a remote household at affordable
ost in comparison to other fuel sources.

There are grants available for the installation of small wind
urbines in the UK. As with all grants there are a number of
tipulations, one of which is that the system must be installed
y an accredited installer. This rules out DIY installation,
lthough it will often be possible for the owner to perform some
f the installation work (where qualified) and logistics, as a
ubcontractor to the installer who will then sign the job off.

In England and Wales, the amount of the grant in pounds is
directly related to the power rating of the turbine in watts. The
smallest eligible size is 500 watts and attracts a £500 grant. As
we shall explain later, the power rating is not a good indicator
of energy production compared with the size of the blade rotor,
and, regrettably, this grant scheme perpetuates the popular
misunderstanding that wind turbine rated power output is the
best measure of what it will do for you.

£1.00 per watt ?

Cost-effectiveness need not be the first criterion! Why
should your wind turbine necessarily compete against cheap
power from polluting engines? When choosing a car, do you
ask how much this will save you in bus fares? The satisfaction
of generating your own power, independently, from a clean
endless source, is hard to quantify. It may be asking too much
to expect it to be the cheapest option as well as the greenest
and most satisfying.

Lifestyle implications

Stand-alone windpower systems are most successful when
the users are enthusiastic and willing to adapt to the changing

moods of the weather. This means moving away from the modern mentality of total convenience, and constant availability, towards living in harmony with your energy supply.

The best time to get around to energy hungry activities, like washing clothes, pumping water, or sanding the floor, is when the weather is windy. When winds are light, it is better to lighten the load on the system, by switching off unnecessary lights. Or you can design a hybrid system, which also includes hydro, solar or diesel generators, for these times.

'Turnkey' windpower systems can be set up to work 'just like the mains' (with automatic generator backup), for those who cannot be bothered with adapting to a limited resource, but these systems are more expensive for the user, as well as for the planet.

Reliability

Although the technology has been around for some time, small-scale windpower systems are still quite thin on the ground in this country, and there has been a pioneering feel about them. As the equipment is so expensive to purchase there is a temptation to buy the cheapest, which, in turn, can lead to disappointment about performance, reliability and/or lifespan.

Even the most expensive renewable energy equipment can go wrong in spectacular and unexpected ways. The user will sometimes need patience as well as enthusiasm. Small wind turbines in particular have a poor record for reliability, which is due to a number of factors. Long running hours take their toll, and a machine designed to be sensitive to a light breeze may suffer badly at the hands of a storm, carrying literally one thousand times as much power, in a wind ten times as fast. Also, wind turbines are poorly understood, so troubleshooting and maintenance are not as simple as with motor cars, for example.

Under the circumstances, the best policy is to cover yourself against all contingencies. Try to talk to someone who has bought and operated similar equipment successfully elsewhere. If possible, buy from a local agent in whom you have confidence. This should not be any more expensive than buying direct from the makers, and it can help greatly with teething troubles and warranty claims. Some installation companies have special vehicles with lifting equipment and tools on board to do installation and servicing in the fastest possible time. Expert attention does improve reliability although it is less fun than getting hands-on yourself.

Most problems with small-scale windpower occur during the first year of operation, and should be sorted out satisfactorily by the suppliers at no extra cost.

The case studies

To help you understand the ideas presented in the book, practical examples will be worked out in four case studies and we shall examine them at the end of each section:

Case study 1: A yacht 12 volt supply

Here, mains power is not available, since the boat is kept on a mooring when not in use. The only engine on board is the outboard motor, which has no electrical output. At weekends, electricity is needed for lighting and small appliances, such as the bilge pump, winch and TV. These can all be run conveniently from a 12 volt battery, which is charged from a very small wind turbine during the week.

Case study 2: A holiday cottage

All the usual electrical equipment will be needed (within reason), since the cottage will be rented out to all comers. The guests cannot be expected to understand the system, so it must be completely automatic in operation (a 'turnkey' system). To give security of supply off-grid under all conditions it may be necessary to use a back-up engine-driven generator from time to time.

Case study 3: A primary school

Again, it is beyond the reach of the national grid. Access is difficult, so it is planned to reduce the amount of heating fuel needed for the building by using the wind for heating. There is also a requirement for electric lighting and power for computers, photocopier and vacuum cleaner.

Electric heaters use much more energy than light and power applications. It is not realistic to use battery power to run heaters. A much cheaper option is to put energy into storage heaters directly from the wind turbine, when there is a surplus beyond what the battery needs. A relatively large wind turbine is needed to produce a useful amount of heat, and this has the added advantage that plentiful power will be available in relatively light winds for charging the battery. So, no back-up generator is needed.

Case study 4: A household on the grid

The house uses 4-5000kWh units of electricity and 20,000kWh of heat per year (the UK average). The site is windy. We need to decide whether to go for a wind heating system, which will offset some of the heating costs, or a grid-connected system, which will reduce the electricity bills. Electricity costs 7 pence per kWh unit and heat costs only 3 pence per kWh (oil fired).

We can also use a heat pump to convert 5,000kWh of electricity into 15,000kWh of heat. This would save a lot of oil but we also need to consider the cost of the wind turbine and the heat pump. How much money and how much energy will it cost to put these in place, and how long will they last?

Section 1: Small wind turbine electrics

The power of the wind has been used for centuries, to take the strain in pushing and shoving applications such as corn grinding and pumping. The relatively recent invention of heat engines (from steam to nuclear) made power available more conveniently, on demand. In the old days, machinery was housed in the windmill, and driven by shafts and gears. Milling and pumping was done as and when the wind blew. Nowadays, we find electricity more convenient than shafts and gears, so wind driven generators are more useful than old-style mills.

Generators work best at high rotational speeds, which is one reason why modern windmill blades move faster than the old windmill sails. The faster they spin, the lighter and cheaper the generator can be, but high blade speed is not always compatible with quiet or trouble-free operation. The best compromise is usually obtained using three rotor blades whose tips travel at about six times the windspeed.

Electricity from windmills is wilder and stranger than electricity from the socket outlets in the home. Small wind systems need to be able to convert windmill power into battery power (or directly to grid power or heat), and then from battery power to domesticated power for our convenience.

In the jargon of electricity, things that use electric power are called 'loads'. System design involves studying these loads and providing for their needs.

Electrical basics

AC and DC power

Almost all electrical generators (whether in power stations or on bicycles) now produce alternating current, known as AC. The current flows to and fro along the wires, rather as the waves flow up and down a beach, but much more rapidly. The mains grid electricity supply is an example of an AC supply. Batteries, on the other hand, operate with direct current (DC), which flows along in a constant direction, more like a river.

Luckily, it is easy to convert AC into DC using a cheap semiconductor device called a rectifier. Rectifiers are often built into the smallest wind turbines so that the output is DC. Larger wind turbines come with control cabinets that are located near to the battery, and the rectifier is located in this cabinet.

Unfortunately, it is much harder to convert DC back into AC, but it is routinely done using an electronic device called an inverter. An inverter is a compact box of electronics, which simply sits and buzzes away to itself, making 'mains' power. Inverters are often used on wind-powered systems to run mains-voltage equipment from batteries. In the case of grid connection without batteries, there are special inverters that synchronise with the grid AC and feed power into the building's electrical system from the high voltage DC output of the turbine.

Voltage

Another important difference between mains electricity and battery power is voltage. Voltage is a measure of the electrical 'pressure drop' between the two wires supplying power. All the equipment on a particular type of supply must have the same voltage rating in order to work properly. The voltage of the supply remains substantially constant, whereas the current varies as power flows from the source to the loads.

In this country, the mains supply is rated at about 240 volts AC, but batteries normally have a much lower voltage: say 12 volts DC, for example. The voltage rating of either sort of supply is nominal, in the sense that it can often vary by as much as 15% without upsetting the loads. As the voltage rises, lights will glow more brightly, and motors will run faster.

The voltage produced by a small wind turbine varies with the speed of rotation. At low speeds, the voltage may not be sufficient to charge a battery or to create grid power. The turbine spins freely at low speeds but no wind energy is converted. As windspeed increases, the voltage rises to a point where it is usable by the system. The alternator winding in the wind turbine is carefully designed – to ensure that the speed of rotation is optimal for the blade rotor to produce the most power when the output voltage reaches that required by the system. If the wind turbine becomes disconnected from the battery (or other load) in strong winds, it will tend to run fast and produce a much higher voltage than during correct operation.

Current

Current is the flow of electrons along a wire; it is measured in amps. Although it flows around the circuit and back to where it started, current transfers energy from A to B. The rate of energy transfer (power) depends on the voltage times the current. At higher voltages, it takes less current to transfer a given amount of energy from the wind turbine to the battery or load. There are limits to the amount of current that a piece of cable can carry.

Using a higher voltage is cheaper than laying more, or thicker cable, when more power is needed.

Cables

Any cable that carries electric current becomes slightly warm. If the temperature rises too far, this is both a waste of power and a potential hazard. To limit the waste heat produced, a thick enough cable must be used. Choosing the best size of cable is discussed on page 66 and in Appendix 3.

Inverters

Stand alone inverters

Power is drawn from the battery through a short, thick cable that can carry a hundred amps or more, and delivered to the loads through longer thinner ones, because the load current is much smaller at the higher voltage. The inverter is kept close to the battery, but not so close as to suffer corrosion from the nasty fumes which batteries give off while on charge. The ideal arrangement is to connect the battery to the inverter with short, thick cables that pass through a wall.

Inverters are expensive to buy, they waste some power during the process of making AC, and they do occasionally go wrong. So it is worth thinking about using 12 volt loads that work directly from the battery instead, thus cutting out the middle man. But all of these drawbacks are diminishing as the technology advances, year by year. Nowadays, inverters have become so cheap, efficient and reliable that it usually makes sense to run the loads on mains-voltage. This opens up a wider choice of lights and appliances, which are often cheaper and

L16 Batteries and Xantrex inverters in a large, American, stand-alone system

more efficient than battery-voltage ones, and standard mains voltage wiring techniques can be used.

Inverters vary in price, power rating, efficiency, waveform and reliability. For £30 or less you can buy a pocket sized inverter that may or may not power a TV. £1500 pays for a programmable 2kW synchronising sine wave inverter, which dances an amazing jig with your back-up generator, see case study 2 on page 41.

Make sure the inverter is powerful enough to meet the peak load on the system, which will usually be the starting surge of a motor. A fridge or freezer motor often draws over ten times its rated power for a second or so, when the thermostat closes and the motor kicks in. This may impose a load of 2kW on the inverter. Most inverters can handle some overload but there will be a dip in voltage, which may crash your computer. On smaller systems the worst surge often occurs when you switch on a colour TV or monitor.

Most modern inverters are designed for high efficiency, but if you plan to buy a big inverter and use it for small loads most of the time, then you should check that it won't be drawing a heavy current from the battery all that time. Inverters for 'UPS' systems for example tend to have a high power consumption when running idle.

Waveform is specified as 'sine wave', 'semi-sine wave', 'square wave' etc. If you can afford it, sine wave power is the one to go for and it is getting more affordable quite quickly. The other waveforms cause funny buzzing noises in many appliances, but they work quite cheerfully in 99% of situations. Certain loads (lamp dimmers, laser printers, some Ni-cad chargers) will not work or may be damaged by anything less than pure sine wave. Every time you plug something new into an inverter is a tiny adventure and another step towards energy self-sufficiency.

It is always good to keep telephone lines away from power lines (50mm) to prevent interference. Where there is a 'modified sine wave' inverter in operation this is especially important. Otherwise there will be a loud buzz when you try to talk with someone on the phone.

Reliability is the hardest thing to assess from the description of an inverter. You can go by reputation or by price: you normally get what you pay for. Very small, lightweight, cheap inverters can be good value for money, but be ready to buy another one at short notice.

Grid connected inverters

Inverters for grid-connection of small wind turbines usually operate with higher voltage DC – around 200 volts. The wind turbine is modified by the manufacturer to produce the appropriate voltage to suit the inverter. A higher voltage means the current is lower (for the same power output) and thinner cables can be used.

Grid connected inverters need to comply with the G83 technical standard, that protects against feeding power back into the grid during power cuts and electrocuting someone. These inverters were usually designed for solar PV (which had been in widespread use for grid connection before small wind) and have been adapted more recently for use with wind turbines.

Inverters can be damaged if the voltage from the turbine rises too high. Wind turbine voltage is very volatile when there is no

Windy Boy inverters are popular for connecting small wind turbines to the grid.

load. Furthermore, these inverters do not put a load on the wind turbine immediately. There are various time delays required by the software and the G83 standard. Some wind turbines have mechanical speed governing devices that limit the speed and hence the voltage, keeping them within safe limits. Others need a voltage clamping circuit, which loads the turbine by dumping power into a heater at a certain voltage, to prevent damage to the inverter.

Batteries

All batteries are built up from units called cells. The voltage of each cell is created by chemical means, and this voltage depends on the chemicals used in its construction. 'Lead-acid' is the commonest type of battery for small windpower systems. Each cell of a lead-acid battery gives 2 volts between terminals. By adding cells in series (end to end) we can build up to 6, 12, 24, 48, 120 or any voltage.

The choice of battery voltage for a windpower system can be fairly arbitrary, but be careful, because once it is made you cannot easily change your mind. The wind turbine, the inverter, and the DC loads must all be rated for this voltage, so that they are correctly matched. 12 volts is a common choice for very small systems. The equipment is cheap and widely available. However 24 volt systems operate at lower current. This will be a better choice when long cable runs or higher power levels are required. 48 volts is even better. The choice will tend to be dictated by available wind turbines, inverters etc and by whether it is desirable to run battery-voltage equipment such as 12-volt lighting.

Much larger batteries are used for windpower than for cars, on the whole. And it does not pay to use automotive engine-starting batteries for a stand-alone system. Car batteries are designed to deliver a high current for a very short time and then be charged up again. They fail quite rapidly if discharged significantly for periods of time. This is called 'deep cycle' duty. There are various types of battery that one can use (see table overleaf).

All of the battery types shown in table overleaf can be found in differing qualities. Battery prices vary considerably, so it is worth searching for a good deal. A no-quibble warranty is valuable. Second-hand batteries can be well worth having, especially the standby type, if the cost is low and safe transport can be arranged. This is a good way to reduce the pollution associated with manufacture and disposal.

Where you need a large battery that will be cycled gently, semi-traction can be a cost-effective solution. Where you have a smaller battery that works hard day by day then a forklift truck battery will stand the pace for much longer. But it may not perform well if left standing for a few weeks, because it tends to lose its charge.

Nickel cadmium batteries are not a great idea because the charging voltage is much higher than the discharge voltage. Wind systems need to operate the loads while charging and discharging. The large voltage range causes problems for some loads. The cadmium in the batteries is also a problem when it comes to safe disposal.

Battery type	Description	Advantages	Cost
'Leisure' or 'semi-traction'	Flat plate heavy duty battery in 12 volt mono-block package	Can be deeply discharged hundreds of times	Cost is low and these batteries are widely available
Valve regulated Sealed lead acid VRSLA	Monoblocks with dry electrolyte made from gel or glass mat	No maintenance. No acid spillage possible. Needs to be charged with care, though	Expensive
Forklift Truck battery or tubular plate traction battery	Usually tall, black single 2-volt cells. Very robust plate construction	Can be deeply discharged on a daily basis for years, but tends to lose charge, especially when older	Expensive
Standby batteries	Single cells in clear cases with large volume of electrolyte	If cycled gently these can last for up to 30 years	Very expensive
Nickel cadmium and Nickel iron (NOT lead acid)	Steel cells at 1.2 volts each	Can be run flat without harm. Work well at low temperatures	Very expensive to buy, and to dispose of (due to toxic cadmium)

Battery system management

The battery will effectively control the system voltage. The wind turbine adapts to the voltage as it finds it. A power surplus causes the voltage to rise, and the battery charges, absorbing the surplus. When the loads start using more power than the

Special 'deep cycle' batteries in 24 volt windpower system. These batteries are sold as separate 2-volt cells.

wind turbine can supply, then the battery voltage drops, and the battery meets the deficit by discharging. The battery should not usually be disconnected from a wind turbine that is running or could run. Voltage from the wind turbine may then rise dangerously high.

25

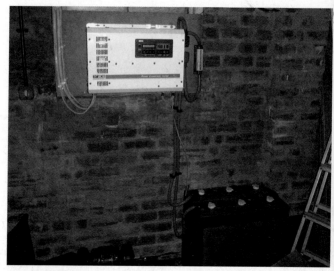

A Xantrex SW inverter/charger connected to a 12 volt forklift truck battery. Forklift batteries are ideal for daily cycling, but less suitable for longer term cycles because they can lose their charge.

As a rule you should avoid discharging lead acid batteries too deeply and leaving them discharged. This will result in sulphation of the plates. Sulphate can be removed by vigorous charging in some cases, but take care not to charge sealed batteries vigorously or they will be damaged.

A low state of charge can be recognised by a drop in voltage, and steps should then be taken to reduce or to cut off the load. Unless there is an engine driven generator connected to the system through automatic controls, then users should be made aware of the battery voltage. Most people will prefer to economise deliberately, rather than have their power cut off unexpectedly. At a certain point, the inverter will shut down to prevent damaging the battery and you will have no power.

Serious stand-alone system users like to have a battery voltmeter situated where they can see it. In the kitchen or hallway are good locations. There are also 'Amp-hour meters' that claim to be able to display the amount of charge in a battery but these are expensive and need very careful calibration to work satisfactorily.

For a 12 volt system, the following guidelines might apply (in relation to the battery voltmeter):

10-11.5 volts: You have a problem. Danger of damage to your battery. Switch off all lights and go to the pub.

11.5-12.5 volts: Switch off all unnecessary lights.

12.5-13 volts: Do as you please.

13-14 volts: Use power profligately.

14-15 volts: Use power frenziedly.

15-16 volts: You have a problem. Danger of damage to loads. Stop the wind turbine, or connect more batteries or heaters.

'Gel' type batteries (with dry electrolyte) will be damaged by prolonged voltages over 14V, but for most batteries a period of overcharge is quite therapeutic from time to time, in moderation. However persistent overcharging, leading to loss of electrolyte and overheating, is not beneficial. Higher voltages can also damage loads on the system, such as inverters.

In practice, nowadays, it is rare to leave battery management to human trial and error. But a degree of awareness on the part of users can mean that the battery lasts much better and gives better service. On the whole, low winds and low battery voltages should be a cue to turn off unnecessary loads, whereas windy weather and high voltage mean that you can comfortably leave things switched on. For example you may wish to turn off the TV/stereo system and computer peripherals when not in use during calm weather as they use significant energy just in standby mode.

Wind turbine 'controllers'

Charge controllers/shunt regulators

The word 'controller' is somewhat ambiguous because it is used to describe both the control box that comes with a wind turbine and a specialised regulator that manages battery charge control by preventing the system voltage from rising above (say) 14 volts.

Most wind/battery systems will come with external controllers that include a rectifier, meters, fuses and the battery voltage regulator. Few turbines come with regulators built in. Some very small turbines use controllers that disconnect the turbine when no more power is wanted for battery charging, but most employ 'shunt' regulators – electronic boxes that control the flow of current to 'shunt' or 'dump' loads, which in turn use up surplus power thereby preventing the voltage from rising higher. The dump load can be a water heater with a thermostat that in turn diverts the power to a space heater when water is hot. Special low voltage heaters are needed for dump loads, or in some cases the wind turbine controller is used to energise mains voltage heaters via the inverter.

A good charge controller will be programmable to the type of battery in use, and will even compensate for battery temperature. But usually the ones supplied with wind turbines are less sophisticated. Solar controllers are not suitable for wind systems, because they control the charging current by disconnecting it when the battery needs no more, but many can be re-configured for 'diversion load' control, which is the same as a dump load regulator. This type of controller operates by high frequency switching of the dump loads, leading to some audible noise in the heaters.

Over-discharge protection

Excessive discharge of the battery can also be dealt with automatically. The simplest solution is a 'low battery cut-out' or 'low voltage cut-out', which will simply disconnect the loads when battery power is exhausted. Inverters will shut themselves down at low battery voltage too. This is probably best left as a last resort, and some more civilised method of power rationing should come into force before the voltage drops to this level.

In situations where the user cannot be expected to participate in energy management by controlling his/her power usage, the best solution is to provide a back-up generator that takes over automatically in the event of a low battery condition.

Inverter/chargers

Where diesel power is routinely used as a back-up to a windpower system, a special sort of combined inverter/charger is often chosen. This type of inverter has a connection to the diesel generator. When the diesel starts up, the inverter automatically transfers all the AC loads over to diesel power. It then changes itself into a battery charger, and feeds power from the diesel back into the battery. This means that the period for which the diesel has to run is limited to a few hours, after which the battery is ready to supply the loads again, regardless of whether the wind has picked up in the meantime. Inverter chargers sometimes contain automatic circuits that will start and stop the generator for you, according to user-defined rules.

Photovoltaic (PV) solar electric panels

Solar electric panels can easily be connected to the system battery, to operate in parallel with the wind turbine. Systems with several sources of power are known as 'hybrid systems' and they have the advantage that there is a better probability that at least one source of power will be available at any given time. Windless periods are often sunny, for example. This more constant supply from two sources means less load on the battery.

A remote area power supply in South Africa with six 6kW Proven turbines and some photovoltaic arrays.

Safety

Electrical safety

With any electrical system we need to guard against the dangers of fire and electric shock by careful design. Electricians are trained to do this in the context of conventional systems but they are unlikely to be familiar with DC systems. Someone has to understand the safety issues clearly at the design stage. What follows is a guide to these issues.

All equipment, including switches and cables in the installation, needs to be able to safely operate at the maximum voltage and maximum current that may arise. Unfortunately these peak values are not usually published by manufacturers, and may even vary from between units that they produce and between sites.

In the event of a fault such as a short circuit, very high currents can flow. To prevent dangerous overload, which might cause fire, a fuse (or a circuit breaker) should be fitted in every circuit. This will blow open before the cable can become too hot. This is called circuit protection. If one wire of the circuit is earthed then a single fuse or breaker will do. If not then both wires should be protected. The size of the wire, its insulation and how it is installed will all affect the choice of fuse or breaker. There are tables in the wiring regulations (reproduced in many places) that refer to circuit protection for PVC insulated cables. If the specified current is not exceeded then the temperature will not exceed 70 degrees, and the insulation will not deteriorate. Thinner wire can sometimes be used if the insulation is appropriate for higher temperatures.

The circuit protection must be chosen so that it can carry any current that will arise even in the most exceptional conditions of correct operation. (Wind turbines sometimes produce unexpectedly high output in storms.) But it must also disconnect the circuit quickly if the current is high enough to overheat the cable. Cables in low voltage systems are usually oversized to avoid energy loss. This makes it easier to select a fuse that will protect the cable.

The current from a short-circuited wind turbine is limited by what the alternator can produce, and in fact short-circuiting may be a routine procedure for braking purposes. If you need to prevent the blades from spinning fast during erection or lowering of the tower for example, you can short-circuit the wires from the alternator (provided you don't short-circuit the battery). Once it is short-circuited the alternator becomes very hard to turn, and so the blades will stall and be unable to spin. The wind turbine cable simply has to be big enough to cope with the turbine's maximum short-circuit current, and the circuit is safe.

But the current from a short-circuited battery can be very high indeed. For this reason, the protection should be fitted close to the battery. Again, when wiring up loads the cables should be connected to the battery through an appropriately sized fuse or circuit breaker (or double pole protection if not earthed). A mains type consumer unit works fine at 12 or 24 volts DC. But take care that the main switch does not disconnect the wind turbine. Automotive fuses and forklift truck fuses are also suitable.

Electric shock is not a hazard in most battery systems because the voltage is too low. But a disconnected wind turbine can produce a voltage several times higher than the battery. The first step toward protecting against electric shock hazard is to make sure that all live wires and connections are housed in boxes out of reach of fingers. The next step is to bond all exposed conductive parts (metal boxes etc) to earth, so that they cannot become live in the event of a loose wire touching them. If the earthing system is bonded to the neutral side of the supply, then a live wire contacting earth will result in a short-circuit that operates the fuse or circuit breaker and disconnects the supply, making it safe.

Mains voltage circuits from the inverter can be treated as mains voltage circuits anywhere, but there are a few important differences. Mains supplies will already have the neutral wire bonded to earth, whereas inverters will not usually have either live wire bonded. It is a good idea to bond the neutral to earth in the distribution board (consumer unit) if it has not been bonded anywhere else, but there should never be more than one bond. Where there is a diesel generator connected, this will often have its own earth-neutral bond. In such cases you should avoid making a second bond elsewhere.

(Some very small, cheap inverters produce a voltage between each of the output wires and the battery negative. If you earth one of the output wires then you will destroy the inverter. Such inverters are not suitable for connection to a domestic wiring system of the UK type.)

The mains grid (like a battery) will be capable of extremely high fault currents in the event of a short-circuit, whereas an inverter has limited ability to deliver current and is actually more likely to shut down when short circuited than to operate the circuit protection. There is no need to obsess about earth loop impedance, because the fault current is so low.

Earthing

There are three types of earthing.

Equipment earthing means that you have a third, earth wire (protective conductor) running with each mains voltage circuit and this is connected to any exposed metalwork in the system. This bonds the external parts together and prevents any hazardous voltage between items. You will not be able to get a shock by touching two pieces of equipment, in the case of a fault in one.

The earth electrode is a buried piece of copper (often just a spike in the ground) that attempts to ensure that the equipment is never at a voltage hazardous to someone who has good contact with the ground. Water and gas pipes are bonded to this electrode at the main earth terminal, and the equipment earthing system (protective conductors) is also linked to this terminal. It is harder than most people realise to get a good earth in the ground. You actually need several earth spikes or better still a quantity of copper buried in a damp place. If the earth electrode is of poor quality (high resistance to earth), then it is advisable to protect the socket outlet circuits with an RCD (earth leakage trip).

Earth bonding of the neutral (often referred to as 'earthing the system') is a third sort of 'earthing'. This is done by connecting the neutral of the supply to earth at one place only in the system, as mentioned above. This should be done where possible so as to make the supply as similar as possible to a UK mains supply. Again, take care not to create a duplicate earth bond. You can tell if there is one in place already, because the voltage between earth and neutral will be zero if there is.

Apart from safety it is a good idea to have good earthing to minimise problems with lightning surges. For this reason it is a good idea to earth the tower (and any guy wires) directly to earth electrodes in the ground. Experts do not agree whether these earth electrodes should be bonded to the earth in the building. Many are in favour of connecting the two electrodes together using buried, bare copper wire. This makes a very good earth in itself and allows any voltage surge to return to earth prior to reaching the building. However, if the building has a mains supply of the PME-type ("protective multiple earthing") then you are not advised to take the building earth outside the 'equipotential zone' of the building. This is because the local network earth can become live in the event of a fault. So if you are on the grid you may be safer not connecting your wind turbine tower to the house earth.

Batteries

Batteries are a health and safety nightmare. Hazards include fire, explosions, acid burns, lead poisoning and spinal damage (when lifting). Keep them in their own shed if possible, with the inverter on the other side of a wall.

Batteries can make big sparks, if you drop a spanner across the terminals, for instance. Keep metal objects away from the battery terminals and cables. This includes personal jewellery, tools, and general junk such as builds up in a shed. A garden spade falling on battery terminals could become red hot and set fire to the building.

Batteries produce hydrogen gas when they are charging. This is very light and will escape through any small hole near the top of the battery enclosure. However if it is trapped in a mixture with oxygen then it can explode. Never smoke nearby or create sparks in the battery compartment. Hydrogen also tends to lurk inside the battery and can be ignited by a spark, say when a crocodile clip is removed. This causes the battery lid to fly off, spattering acid and broken plastic shards into the eyes of the person holding the clip.

Batteries need to be topped up periodically with de-ionised water to replace the water consumed in making hydrogen. If they are not topped up and the plates become exposed, then the plates will deteriorate. In extreme cases, when the plates degrade to the point where they start to contact each other, the resultant spark can cause the cell to explode and damage the neighbouring cells, which may also explode. This makes quite a mess.

Spilt acid can be neutralised with soda crystals. Sulphuric acid is biodegradable in any case. Lead is a persistent poison however, so damaged or dead batteries should not be discarded carelessly. The sediment is toxic. Batteries should always be taken for recycling, and not disassembled or drained.

Finally, the lead in batteries is very heavy and can damage your back if you are careless while lifting or placing them in a confined space. Take care to plan how to move them and avoid the painful consequences. Tall cells on a pallet are often quite unstable as well and should be carefully braced against falling over if the pallet is moved abruptly. Acid on clothing will make holes. Acid in the eyes can do much worse harm. The treatment is flushing in water for a long period.

Protect yourself and others. Battery accidents are rare and easily prevented.

Signs and diagrams

You should put warning signs on the battery compartment and on electrical boxes that are energised by the wind system. Renewable energy systems can be confusing, with various sources of power that may not be easy to isolate. A clear diagram showing location of fuses etc. should be on the wall in case someone else has to try to understand how it works one day.

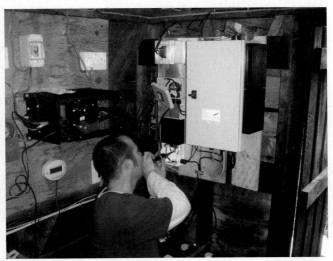

Typical battery-shed wiring for a standalone system.

The case studies

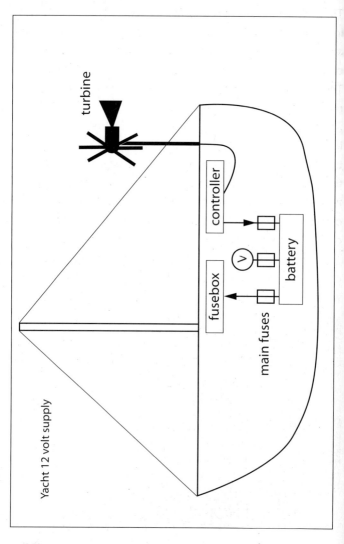

Case study 1

This is a fairly minimal system, containing the basic ingredients for generation (wind turbine), storage (battery), and control (shunt regulator and fuse box). The wind turbine produces energy at the required voltage, but only when the wind blows. This energy is fed to the battery, which accumulates it until it is required by the loads.

In the event that the battery is 'full', surplus energy is diverted into heating by the shunt regulator. This prevents damage to the battery and the loads, which would otherwise occur due to the system voltage rising too high. The fuse box is also used for protection, in this case against the consequences of a short circuit in the wiring, which could otherwise cause cables to overheat, starting a fire.

No controls are necessary to prevent the battery being run down, since the owners will be monitoring the situation by watching the voltmeter.

LVM turbines are popular for boats and caravans.

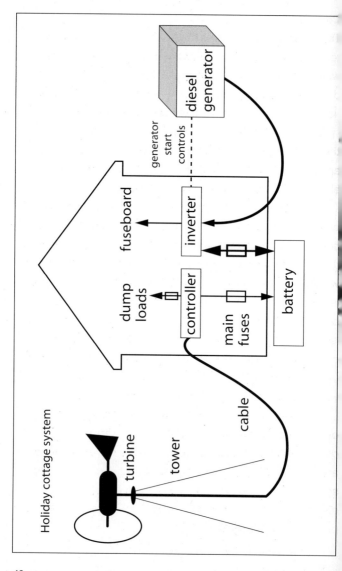

Holiday cottage system

Case study 2

The holiday cottage system is much more complicated, in order to make life simpler for the occupants. Again, energy from the wind turbine is accumulated in a battery, and surplus energy is diverted to heat. Since this is a larger system, a small heater is used, which is separate from the controller as such.

The biggest difference is that light and power circuits in the cottage are fed with mains-voltage, so that conventional appliances can be plugged in. The inverter converts the electricity from 24 volts to mains-voltage.

To provide fully automatic operation, a special type of programmable inverter is used, which monitors battery condition and power consumption. If more power is required than either the battery or inverter can provide, then the inverter will automatically start up a diesel generator. When the diesel is running, the inverter synchronises with it and maintains a constant load on it. If the engine is under-loaded, the surplus is used for battery charging, 'back-fed' through the inverter. If overloaded, the inverter will assist the diesel, drawing power from the battery. This makes best use of the diesel generator while it is running, and fuel consumption is minimised.

The cable from the wind turbine to the house is buried in a deep trench. Alongside this is a heavy, bare copper wire that is connected at both ends to the earthing terminals of the tower and the building. The earth is bonded to neutral in the generator, so there is no need to bond the neutral elsewhere. Power is distributed from a conventional split consumer unit with RCD protection for the socket outlets.

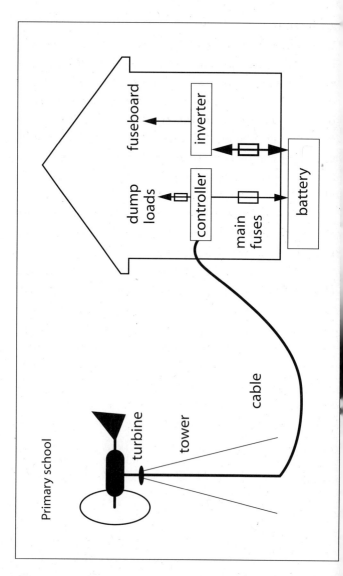

Case study 3

The primary school has a relatively simple system. The wind turbine is much larger again (6kW) and provides much more energy than is needed for lighting and power. The controller dumps about 80% of the incoming energy into space heaters over the course of the year. However, it never diverts any energy to heat unless the battery is receiving its optimum charging current already. This ensures that the battery is always kept well charged, even in periods of relatively low windspeed, and so no back-up generator is needed.

In case studies 2 and 3, the inverter and control equipment are wall-mounted in a shed. The controller and the inverter need to be protected from the weather and from the corrosive fumes that the battery may produce. The inverter especially needs ample ventilation, and may be quite noisy in operation, so careful thought needs to go into the location of these items. A control cubicle housing the control equipment, inverter and fuse-box is normally erected adjacent to the battery but not in the same compartment. This must be of sound construction in areas of high windspeed, because entry of rain or snow will cause serious damage to the electronics.

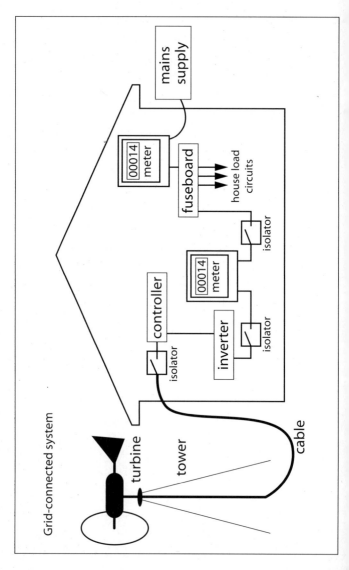

Grid-connected system

Case study 4

Let's assume that a grid-connected system is chosen. The electrical system is physically very simple to install. The turbine is of a type that limits its speed automatically, so the voltage will never exceed the 400 volts limit set by the inverter manufacturer. The grid-connect inverter is a large cabinet, about 400mm x 600mm, but there are no batteries and the rest of the control gear simply consists of a rectifier in the controller and various switches and meters all provided with the wind turbine.

The tower needs to be earthed well for lightning and for safety. An electrode resistance lower than 10 ohms is required, and this will involve some expensive excavation and installation of copper strips and rods in the soil. This assembly must not be connected to the earth terminal in the dwelling because the district network uses PME (protective multiple earthing). In PME systems the neutral wire of the supply is also the earth wire. If this wire breaks then the earth electrode ends up carrying high currents and the earthed wires become unsafe to touch outside of the 'equipotential zone' in the building.

Section 2: Assessing your needs

Energy and power

In order to assess your needs you need to understand the exact meanings of the two words 'energy' and 'power'. Energy is the 'stuff' produced by a wind turbine. Energy is what you pay for in your electricity bill, if you are unlucky enough to have one. The unit of electrical energy is the kilowatt-hour (kWh).

Power is the rate of production of energy, measured in watts or kilowatts. One kilowatt (kW) is 1,000 watts. If a heater uses 2 kilowatts of power for 2 hours, then it will have consumed 4kWh of energy. There is no such thing as a 'kilowatt per hour'. This would make as much sense as talking about mph per hour, when you mean a mile.

The first question that most people ask about a wind turbine is 'How much power can it produce?' This is actually the wrong question. You should ask, 'How much energy can it produce?' Energy is the bottom line. Energy equates to money in the bank. Power is the rate of production, but the wind fluctuates constantly and so does the power output of a turbine.

Power means nothing unless it is sustained over a period of time. Energy production is achieved by cranking out watts for hours. The hours are just as important as the watts.

In the case of stand-alone systems it is equally important to know both the power requirements of a load and the hours for which it will run. Then you can calculate the energy it will use. Assuming that there is battery storage in the windpower system, it is not necessary to match the power output of the wind turbine to the power required by the load. Both of these power levels will vary in a complicated way, depending on wind conditions and user activity. Successful system design depends on matching energy supply over a period of time to the energy requirements of the user.

In this section we shall discuss methods of estimating the energy requirements of some typical loads.

We list the loads along with their power consumptions and likely hours of use, so that we can calculate the energy consumption for each load. This can be an interesting exercise, especially for the purpose of comparing the energy costs of different loads, but the answers will always be approximate. Given an approximate idea of the energy we shall need, we can match this up to an even more approximate estimate of the energy we expect to get from the wind turbine on our chosen site. This will help us to choose the best wind turbine for the job. An allowance should always be made for losses in the cable, battery, inverter and dump loads (say 30% overall loss).

Often the resulting choice will be too expensive and then it will be necessary to look hard at the list of loads. Sometimes it is possible to use windpower in windy weather and then revert to other fuels in calms.

The first step is to choose a time period over which to study our energy demand. This should be a day or a week, as longer periods are not realistic in terms of battery storage. Next we make up a table with 4 columns. (See the load tables for the case study examples on pages 52-54).

In column 1 put the name of the load.

In column 2 put the power rating. This will be in watts or kW.

In column 3 put an estimate of the average hours per week it will be in use.

In column 4 multiply the entries from columns 2 and 3, to give energy demand in kWh.

NB If the entry in column 2 was watts rather than kW then we need to divide by 1,000.

Some loads have two very different modes of operation. For example, a fax machine may use 50 watts when printing out, for a minute or two, but during its standby mode it only uses about 10 watts.

Often the hardest part to answer is column 3, the hours. If the load is a fridge, for example, then it will turn itself on and off, depending on the temperature and the number of times the door is opened. The only accurate way to measure the energy consumption of some loads is to use an electricity meter. But you can also find out the manufacturer's rating in kWh per day in most cases.

By totalling the figures in column 4, you can estimate your total energy needs over one week. This helps you to choose the right size of wind turbine. You will need to do this for both the summer and winter months.

You can also use this information to help with choice of battery capacity. There are two basic specifications for a battery: voltage and capacity in amp-hours. Multiplying volts by amp-hours gives the battery capacity in watt-hours. Divide this by 1,000 to obtain the kWh capacity of the battery. Compare this figure with the energy needs in kWh/week, and you can see how many days reserve the battery offers. A battery capacity sized to last between 3 days and a week is desirable. When

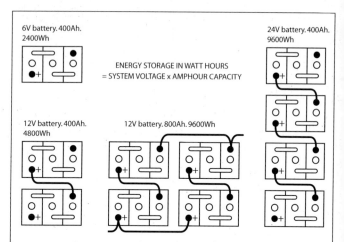

A battery has two basic specifications: voltage and capacity in amphours.

Multiply them to find the watt-hours of energy storage.

For example: a 12 volt battery with 400 amphour capacity holds 12 x 400 = 4800 Watt-hours (4.8kWh) of energy.

Each of the above 6 volt batteries would weigh about 50kg and cost £150.

Battery storage weighs about 20kg and costs about £60 per kWh of total energy.

But you must never run your battery completely flat as this will cause damage.

Plan to use about 60% of the capacity on a regular basis. A budget price would be about £100 per kWh unit of energy stored.

Cost dictates the size of the battery in most cases, but a useable storage of about 3-4 days worth of energy is often a good target.

sizing battery banks you should only aim to use 50-80% of this capacity routinely to prevent damage to the battery (depending on type).

Batteries are often grouped together to increase their capacity. A string of 400Ah cells makes a 400Ah battery. More amphours can be gained by connecting more strings in parallel (joining the positives together and the negatives together so they are at the same voltage and share the current).

Energy capacity : Watt-hours = Volts x Amphours
Example:
12 volts 400Ah makes
12 x 400 = 4800 Watt hours (4.8kWh)

The table of loads also helps with choosing a suitable inverter.

Here we look at power requirements rather than energy. Loads that run from the battery require no inverter, and there is almost no limit to the amount of power that the battery can deliver at any given instant (given adequate cables). Loads that run from the inverter need to be looked at in terms of the maximum load that they will put on the inverter if used simultaneously. The inverter should be chosen to meet this load comfortably, so as to maintain good power quality.

How this applies to the case studies...

Case study 1: A yacht 12 volt supply

The loads are mostly quite modest. The cabin is quite small, and 12 volt lighting is very efficient, so 20 watt bulbs are bright enough. Halogen spot lamps can be used to create a very cosy atmosphere, with very bright pools of light where needed.

The electric winch uses a lot of power, but since it is only used for a brief period of time, the energy consumption per week is very small.

Load name	Power (watts)	Hours per week	Energy kWh/week
4 Interior lights @ 20W each	80	10	0.8
Lights (navigation)	60	4	0.24
Bilge pump	50	2	0.1
Portable T.V.	50	4	0.2
Electric winch	700	1/6	0.117
Total			1.457
+ 30% to cover losses			0.437
Total			**1.894**

Battery voltage: 12V
Capacity: 200 amp-hours, giving 12Vx200/1000 = 2.4kWh
Of this capacity only 80% should be used, giving 1 week's supply.

Case study 2: A holiday cottage

We need to keep energy use to a minimum, since it would be very
expensive to provide the amount used by a typical household
on the mains (about 30kWh per head per week). With a
little attention to energy conservation this can be cut right
down.

- No electric heaters are provided, as there is good insulation
  and an efficient wood fired heating system.
- Compact fluorescent lights are used in place of normal
  'incandescent' light bulbs. These lamps cost more to buy,
  but only use a fraction of the power to give the same light
  level.

Load name	Power (watts)	Hours per week	Energy kWh/week
5 Compact fluorescent lamps @ 20W each	100	40	4
T.V. (20" colour)	100	40	4
Vacuum cleaner	800	1	0.8
Washing machine	2,000	1	2.0
Total			10.8
+ 30% to cover losses			3.24
Total			**14.04**

Battery voltage: 24V
Capacity: 416 amp-hours, giving about 10kWh
In this case the presence of the diesel engine generator makes battery
capacity less critically important. The battery would last about 4 days
(80%=8kWh).

Case study 3: A primary school

Here, we have two different classes of load. The heaters use 3kW, but they do not run from the battery, so we can ignore them in our calculation of storage capacity. The other loads all run from the battery through the inverter.

The fluorescent tubes that the Education Authority uses for classroom lighting are not compatible with a 'semi-sine wave' inverter, which causes buzzing and flickering. Proper sine wave is needed. This could be provided by filtering the semi-sine wave with a 'sine wave filter', but it is found that the filter would draw 300 watts of power on its own. Although this sort of energy loss would be tolerable on a system with such a large wind turbine it is decided to use the latest 'state-of-the-art' sine wave inverter for the job, giving both high efficiency and pure sine wave.

Load name	Power (watts)	Hours per week	Energy kWh/week
5 Fluorescent tube lights	500	40	20
Computer systems	200	15	0.3
Water heater	2000	1	2
Vacuum cleaner	1000	2	2
Photocopier	1200	1.5	1.8
Total			26.1
+ 30% to cover losses			7.83
Total			**33.93**
Battery voltage: 120V			
Battery capacity: 450 amp-hours, giving 54kWh			
80% of 54 = 43.2kWh, which is nine days supply			

Case study 4: The grid-connected house

In this case the grid will provide back-up for any extra power that is needed, so we can be flexible about energy consumption. The electricity meter and bills will give data for electricity usage. But it is still useful to think in terms of analysing which loads are using how much of your energy. Energy conservation is a much easier way to save electricity than small scale wind energy.

Section 3: Siting small wind turbines

A broadband relay station powered by an Ampair turbine and some PV. This is a good site for a small wind turbine.

The power output of a wind turbine is entirely dependent on the wind you expose it to, and this will depend on the site. We need to look at the site carefully; firstly to assess how much energy the wind turbine may produce and secondly to find the best exact location for the wind turbine.

Site windspeed assessment

Most people, if asked, will venture the opinion that they live in a really windy place. Perhaps this is because when the wind blows hard it is an impressive natural force. Unfortunately, few sites are really sufficiently windy on a regular basis for wind turbines to be viable. For example, sites among tall trees and buildings are not appropriate, unless the wind turbine can be placed on a very tall tower or on the roof of a tower block. The jury is still out on the tower block idea.

The most important criterion for a windpower site is the mean (average) windspeed. This is quoted in metres per second (m/s). (For comparison, 5m/s is about 11 mph.) Actual windspeed will vary widely from the average figure, but the frequency with which any higher or lower windspeed will be encountered can be calculated with some accuracy from this average.

Given this information, and some accurate specifications for the wind turbine, it is possible to predict the energy to be generated in an average day, week or whatever time interval you have chosen to total your energy needs over. Turbine manufacturers will give estimates of energy production on various sites in their literature, but beware of a tendency to optimism in these estimates.

As a rough guide, below is a table of approximate weekly energy figures for typical wind turbines in five sizes.

Energy in kWh per week for 5 sizes of wind turbine at different annual mean windspeeds					
swept area	3m/s	4m/s	5m/s	6m/s	7m/s
1m diameter	1	2	4	7	9
2m diameter	3.5	9	17	26	36
3m diameter	8	20	40	60	80
4m diameter	14	35	70	100	140
5m diameter	22	56	106	164	220

Finding the average windspeed is not easy, however. To measure it accurately, you would need to put an anemometer (windspeed measuring instrument) on the site for at least one year, preferably for several. Alternatively, a short term measurement programme can be correlated with long term data from nearby meteorological stations to produce an acceptable result.

The anemometer and its associated data-logging equipment could cost more than a small wind turbine. Where a multi-million pound wind farm project is at stake, then such a study is essential, but for a domestic situation it would be disproportionate. Lower cost anemometry is possible, but for most people it is more realistic to make an estimate of the site's average windspeed, based on the location, the ground conditions and the height of the tower.

Hilltop sites will be much better for wind energy than sheltered valleys. Ground conditions can also be a guide to average windspeed. The 'roughness' is the degree of shelter from trees, buildings, etc. A simple classification system exists, as follows:

Category	Meaning
0	Open water
1	Open areas without significant windbreaks
2	Farmland with windbreaks at least 1000m apart
3	Urban districts, forests, areas with many windbreaks

Effect of 'Roughness' on windspeed		
Roughness category at	10m or	20m height
0	6.9m/s	7.5m/s
1	5.5m/s	6.2m/s
2	4.7m/s	5.5m/s
3	3.5m/s	4.5m/s

Where there is a change in roughness, windspeed will change only gradually. So for example, even though they are not actually located on open water, sites near the sea will be windier than similar inland sites.

In simple cases, where the terrain conforms with one of these categories for large distances in all directions, and hills are not significant, we can estimate windspeeds as shown in the table above.

There is a web page at the DTI website (search for 'windspeed') that can give windspeed estimates for any kilometre square in the country. Estimates are at any or all of three heights: 10m, 25m or 45m above ground, at the site. In most cases the 10 metre data will be most relevant – take care not to be distracted by the high windspeeds at 45 metres height because you will not be able to afford the tower. The figures for surrounding squares are helpful in showing the variations with local ground conditions (slopes mostly), which will also vary within one square. Local shelter conditions will also have an effect. Use the DTI figures as a starting point only. Urban or wooded locations may have dramatically lower winds than the DTI would estimate.

A 2.5kW turbine above treetop level on a 20 metre tower.

Poorly sited wind turbine.
This Rutland turbine will not get much wind.

This Rutland turbine has been sited above surrounding trees and buildings. The tall tower is expensive but essential for a successful result.

Tower position and height

The table of windspeeds above tells an important story about the selection of tower height. In open situations the windspeed is not greatly increased by using a 20m tower rather than a 10m tower. (The increase is about 10%.) In more sheltered places, the increase is dramatic (20-30%). This can make the difference between the success and failure of the whole project. Windpower depends on the cube of windspeed, so if windspeed is increased 26%, power is doubled!

Turbulence

Quality of wind, as well as quantity, is better at greater height. This may seem an odd statement to make, but wind does in fact have structure. A smooth, steady flow is much better than a broken, gusty one.

When wind encounters obstacles, it is not simply slowed down. Parcels of air become separated from each other, and swirl off in different directions. The process is known as 'vortex shedding'. When the obstacle is a small one, like a telephone wire, the vortices are small and rapidly alternating. They are the source of the humming noise that wires emit in the wind. A large block of trees or a building will produce much slower oscillations of wind, on a timescale of several seconds. These patterns of turbulence can be examined by flying a kite in the wake of obstacles to the wind. Turbulence extends over a surprisingly large space in the lee of a house, for example. The zone affected will rise to about twice the height of the building and stretch to a horizontal distance of over ten times that height downwind, with a zone of extreme turbulence up to four times the height downwind. Gradually the airflow will 'recombine'

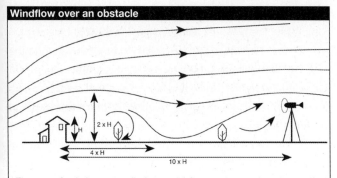

Windflow over an obstacle

H

2 x H

4 x H

10 x H

The zone of turbulence actually rises as the flow progresses downstream. If the obstacle is a building, then it should not block the prevailing wind. If you have a block of trees near the site, then you may find better wind above the trees than away from them.

windspeed, even at double the height above ground and ten times that distance downwind (see diagram, above).

Another source of turbulent flow is steep slopes, buildings or cliffs. Again, the airflow will separate from the ground at sudden changes of gradient. If you stand well back from the edge of a cliff, you will feel the wind constantly changing, and sometimes it may even reverse and blow the opposite way!

Turbulence interferes with the proper operation of wind turbines. The machine finds itself facing in the wrong direction, or running at the wrong speed to make best use of the sudden gusts of wind that it encounters. Constant re-orientation puts a strain on the blade materials and wears out the bearings. Not only will energy capture be disappointing but the life of the machine may be seriously reduced.

Sites for small wind turbines are nearly always near to buildings of some sort, and may also be close to trees and even steep cliffs. In the real world we cannot avoid these obstacles completely. The simplest advice is: put the wind turbine as high as possible. This will reach the best windspeeds and stand the best chance of avoiding turbulence. Wind turbines vary in their ability to survive turbulence and some American manufacturers recommend a minimum tower height of 18m, with options up to 45m! This makes good economic sense too, because the energy capture will be much better. In the UK there may be problems getting planning permission for very high towers, but if not they are well worth considering.

Tower types

A 'tower' is anything that can be used to support the wind turbine. Most people would prefer a tower without guys (a 'free standing' tower), but a guyed tower is usually chosen on grounds of cost. Very satisfactory, low cost, guyed towers can

Erection of the 15 metre tower by hand, using a Tirfor rope hoist.

A Bornay Inclin 1500 turbine on a low cost 'tilt-up' tower made from steel waterpipe.

be constructed with standard lengths of steel waterpipe, and many small wind machines are designed to fit such pipe.

In the UK it is normal practice to attach the wind turbine to the tower before erection, and then to hoist the whole thing up, using a small winch. It is equally possible for an experienced climber to assemble the turbine at the top. Either way, it is most important to keep observers and passers-by well clear in case anything falls. Lifting operations need to be carefully planned so that all concerned know exactly what to expect.

Cable type

Battery charging wind turbines normally operate at low voltages such as 12 or 24 volts. Under these conditions, thick cables are needed in order to minimise power loss. The longer the cable, the heavier it must also be, so the cost increases approximately with the square of the distance covered. This will be an incentive to keep the wind turbine close to the point of use.

Steel Wire Armoured cable (SWA), which looks rather like black plastic waterpipe, is the best choice for outdoor jobs as it can be buried directly in the soil. Purchased new, armoured cable will cost between £5 and £10 per metre and costs are rising rapidly. See Appendix 3 for details of calculations for cable sizes. In the table opposite are some useful figures. Note that 24V system cables can carry four times as much power. The table tells you the maximum cable run in metres.

Good prices for new cable are advertised in *Exchange & Mart*. Even better deals can be made with your local non-ferrous metals dealer, who may have lengths of armoured cable to dispose of. Reusing it is better for the pocket and the environment.

If several pieces are to be strung together then good connections are essential. The best way to connect the wires is by crimping them. Small bore copper tubes cut into short pieces are perfect low cost crimp connectors. Strip about 3cm of wire bare and stuff the ends you wish to join into pieces of tube, side by side in the same direction…the tighter the fit the better. Then crimp the join by crushing the pipe with pliers or vice grips. Attacking it with a blunt punch and a hammer is good. You can even use a proper crimping tool if you can afford a heavy duty one costing about £100. Tie the two armoured

Maximum lengths for cables							
Wind turbine Rating	Copper cable size						
	1.5mm²	2.5mm²	4mm²	6mm²	10mm²	16mm²	25mm²
60W at 12V or 240W at 24V	22m	36m	58m	86m	144m	230m	360m
250W at 12V or 1kW at 24V	DO NOT USE THESE SIZES		11m	21m	35m	55m	86m

Maximum length in metres for 20% power loss at full power output (average losses will actually be less).

cables together below the joint, and tape each connection up generously to insulate them. If the joint is kept above ground and protected from rain with a plastic bottle or suchlike then it will give years of trouble-free service.

Other considerations

Safety
Towers should never be erected where they can possibly contact overhead, high-voltage cables. They should not be erected over public pathways or play areas. Parts can and do fall off small wind turbines. It is even remotely possible that the whole tower will collapse! The consequences must be minimised in advance.

Planning
This paragraph is taken from the British Wind Energy Association (BWEA) web page:

'Planning Policy Statement 22 (PPS22) sets out a clear national policy framework on renewable energy for planning authorities in England to ensure that the Government's renewable energy targets are met. Under PPS22 regional and Local Planning

Authorities should recognise the full range of renewable energy sources, their differing characteristics, locational requirements and the potential for exploiting them subject to appropriate environmental safeguards. Small scale developments can also be permitted within areas such as National Parks, Areas of Outstanding Natural Beauty and Heritage Coasts provided that there is no serious environmental detriment to the area concerned. PPS22 introduces a new policy area for small systems by encouraging Local Planning Authorities to require that new developments should supply a percentage of their energy needs from from on-site renewable energy sources.'

Planning consent should be easy, but local attitudes can cause delays. A chat on the phone with a planning officer is often quite rewarding and costs very little.

Visibility

Wind turbines are very high profile developments. Most people seem to like them, but not everyone does. A sensitive attitude to your neighbours is not only good manners but could well save you considerable trouble later. Look at the planned site from their point of view. Does it obstruct their favourite view? Will reflections or shadows from the blades cause an irritating flicker in their windows?

Noise

Wind turbines make two sorts of sound: blade swish and mechanical hum. These can become 'noise' when the level is intrusively high. This will depend on background noise levels. Background noise can be very low indeed in remote places, when the wind is not strong. If sited near a road, where traffic noise dominates, the wind turbine would not be audible, but in quiet conditions it could cause a nuisance to some people. Tonal noises, such as humming from the alternator, are more audible than blade swish. Wind turbines mounted on buildings and other structures will produce resonances within these structures.

Rooftop mounting

Mounting wind turbines on roofs is not usually a good idea. Noise transmission through the building is only one of the problems. It may be difficult to find a mounting arrangement that will not damage the building structure when strong winds buffet the turbine. Winds at rooftop level are always turbulent, and far from ideal for safe and efficient operation of wind turbines. Access for installation and maintenance will be challenging in most cases.

Swift turbines. Winds are weak and turbulent at rooftop level.

In spite of the above, there is great enthusiasm for rooftop mounted wind turbines at the time of writing. Prominent public figures are buying them from large public utility companies in the confident expectation of making useful savings on their electricity bills. This is a worrying trend. Time will tell whether this type of product is successful. It is more likely that these turbines will prove to be expensive toys. It would be more sensible to mount them on proper towers clear of obstructions, so that they can realise their full energy potential.

How this applies to the case studies

Case study 1: A yacht 12 volt supply

The yacht is to be moored in an anchorage. Although it is by the sea, it is among a cluster of other boats and the south side of the harbour faces a large town. We can estimate the average windspeed at about 5m/s at mast-head height. Referring to the table on page 58 we see that a wind turbine with a diameter of 1 metre might therefore give us around 4kWh/week. This is well above our projected energy consumption. There are plenty of machines to choose from around this size, but the question is: can we hoist one up to the mast top? There will be much less power available at deck level.

Case study 2: A holiday cottage

Our holiday cottage is high in the hills but far from the coast, and the DTI database predicts a windspeed of 4.5m/s at our 10 metre tower height. Allowing for the shelter effect of a plantation of trees 100 metres to the north, we decide to say 4m/s. The table on page 58 shows that a 3 metre diameter machine would provide about 20kWh/week, which would meet the full demand, in theory. However, the budget will not stretch that far, and since there has to be a diesel generator in the system anyway, we opt for a machine of about 2 metre rotor diameter, giving an estimated 9kWh/week. This should save a lot of diesel fuel, and will probably keep the house going on its own in winter, when there are fewer visitors and the wind is strong.

Case study 3: A primary school

The school is in a windy place, beside the sea on the west coast, so the prevailing wind comes in over the water. We can estimate an average windspeed of 6m/s at our 15 metre tower height. To provide serious heating input to the building, a 5 metre diameter machine has been chosen. The table shows this will give about 164kWh in an average week, which is almost 1kW average power (there are 168 hours in a week)! In the winter, when heat is needed most, the figure should be well above this. Even in summer time we can be practically sure of the 26kWh that we have estimated we need for light and power. After all, the days are brighter in summer, and the school can do without lights altogether if the weather is exceptionally calm.

Case study 4: A grid-connected house

The house is in a built-up environment. The DTI database returns a mean windspeed of 5.8 metres per second at 10 metre height. But there are buildings 10 metres high all around and so the wind is severely affected by these. The turbine should really be placed on a 20 metre tower to avoid turbulence and to reach a good wind. But the manufacturer of our preferred turbine only offers towers up to 11 metres tall. A special 20 metre tower would be too expensive. Instead we look at rooftop mounted turbines. We find one with a diameter around 2 metres that claims to produce 50kWh per week at very low installed cost, but looking at the table this claim seems unrealistic. Finally we opt for a 3 metre diameter turbine of a different make again, because it is compatible with an affordable 20 metre tower. This will give the best return on investment because it can be placed in an adequate windspeed. But it remains to be seen if we can get planning approval for our project.

Section 4: Understanding wind turbine specifications

French Vergnet turbines power the remote island of Muck.

A small wind turbine consists of an electrical generator driven by a set of rotor blades. The rotor blades are nearly always directly coupled to the generator. Only rarely are gearboxes used on small machines. The machine swivels to face into the wind, usually moved by a tail at the back. Cables connect the wind turbine to the control panel, usually through a swivelling connection, via brushes and sliprings.

When choosing a wind turbine you will check out web sites, or be given leaflets describing the various products. Data from these sources was used to compile the tables in Appendix 2. Specifications are given under these standard headings, explained below.

Model

The name of the particular turbine. Often includes a number, which may refer to any or none of the specifications below.

Glen Affric Youth Hostel is powered by a 2.5kW turbine and some PV.

Manufacturer

Some have been around for decades whereas others have not yet put their turbines up for sale on the open market, in spite of months of bold publicity.

Nationality

UK produced machines have a head start, but imported machines can be surprisingly cheap. Bear in mind that you get ~~what you pay for.~~ Quality, reliability and durability are all just as important as price in the end. Look for an experienced distributor who you can call upon for help in years to come if necessary.

Price £ (inc. 17.5 % vat)

Some wind turbines are sold 'bare' with a range of optional controllers etc. Others are sold as packages. This makes price comparisons more difficult, but with careful research you can compare prices for the package that suits you best. Prices here are quoted inclusive of 17.5% VAT but a system installed by a professional will only attract 5% tax.

Included in price

In most cases there will be a charge regulator included. In some cases I could only obtain prices for complete systems.

Rotor diameter

Measured in metres (m), rotor diameter is the size of the circle swept by the 'propeller' or blade rotor, measured from one side to the other. Experts agree that rotor diameter is the important criterion for gauging the productivity of the wind turbine. Energy capture is roughly proportional to the square of the diameter (reflecting the swept area). This specification can tell you more about the wind turbine than its rated power. A large rotor diameter should mean plenty of power, assuming that the machine is reasonably efficient. See also the table in the previous chapter with plausible energy estimates for different sized rotors.

Energy at 5m/s site

To compare one turbine with another, you must look at the energy they produce over a period of time on a typical site. In the appendix we quote kWh per week. This is an average figure. Any single week will vary widely from another. Energy production is really the bottom line for the value of the wind turbine (while it is working). If your site windspeed is better or worse then you will get better or worse results. Be aware however that the data quoted here is from manufacturers' literature. The actual machine you buy will probably give less energy if you measure it.

The power curve

The power curve of the wind turbine is a graph produced by the makers that shows the power output at any windspeed. Many of the specifications below are also points on this graph. Sadly, this curve is not often subject to independent tests. It can owe more to fantasy than reality, and often shows performance exceeding the maximum possible in theory. Design of small wind energy systems is made very difficult by the lack of properly authenticated data about wind turbine performance.

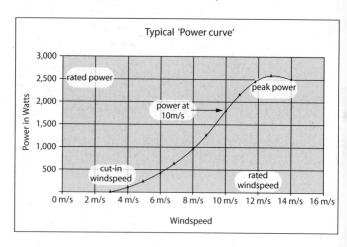

Cut-in windspeed (m/s)

Measured in metres per second (m/s) this is the lowest windspeed that produces any power. If the wind is below cut-in, then the blades may turn, but the voltage is not sufficient for electrical generation. It is good news if the cut-in windspeed is low, because this means you are in business for more of the time. Even a small output is better than none at all, especially

The Iskra 6kW turbine is upwind with pitch controlled blades.

for stand-alone systems where wind may be the only source of energy. In most cases the cut-in windspeed will be 3 m/s. Lower windspeeds carry hardly any energy.

Power at 10m/s

It can be interesting to compare one turbine against another at 10m/s windspeed. This creates a level playing field.

Rated windspeed

This is the windspeed at which the wind turbine will produce its rated power. It is usually somewhere between 10 and 15m/s. The lower it is, the more hours per year the wind turbine will achieve its rated power. High rated power is no advantage if the rated windspeed is also very high (and therefore very rare). A small machine with high rated windspeed will produce high rated power for its size. But a larger machine with a low rated windspeed will produce a lot of energy in relation to its rated power. And the energy supply will be less erratic.

Rated power

Expressed in watts (W) or kilowatts (kW), this is the amount of energy delivered per hour, under ideal wind conditions (see 'rated windspeed'). This is the most quoted statistic for a wind turbine, but it is not as useful as the energy production. Rated power is usually the power output at windspeeds close to where the machine begins to govern or furl so as to limit its output.

Peak power

It is important to know the peak power that the machine can produce in order to safely design the wiring. Peak power can be well above rated power in some cases where the mechanical controls are crude. There is some confusion about what the peak power actually means, and in reality the peak tends to vary with individual machines and sites.

High power is exciting but not always convenient. It will only occur rarely in very high winds. Steady power is more useful.

Rated rpm

This is the speed of shaft rotation at which rated power is produced. A high rpm enables lighter generator construction, but can cause other problems. When the blade tips travel very fast, then there is more noise and more wear of the blade material. Tip speed can be calculated from the rpm and the rotor diameter (see Appendix 3 for the formula).

Attaching blades to a Proven 600W turbine on a 5.5 metre tilt-up tower.

Application

Until recently the biggest demand was for battery charging. Heating and pumping options were also sold for cold or dry locations. At the time of writing the grid-linked option is suddenly very popular. Most gridlinked systems are based on third party inverters from German sources.

Voltages

Voltage is important for reasons of compatibility with other equipment, such as battery, inverter, and loads. 12 or 24 volts are common choices for battery based systems, and 48 volts is becoming popular for larger systems or longer cable runs. Higher voltages are used for heating purposes or for grid connection. The wind turbine 'voltage' is nominal. The actual voltage can vary considerably. Losses in the cables or in poor connections

Ian Woofenden

A Bergey XL 10kW turbine. 30 metre towers are commonplace in the USA.

or other defects between the wind turbine and the battery will result in higher voltage at the wind turbine. A disconnected wind turbine will run fast and produce much higher voltage than its rated output. This can be a hazard, especially in higher voltage machines. Wiring must be treated with respect.

Generator type

Most small wind turbines now use permanent magnet alternators (PMAs). The AC from the alternator is converted to DC for battery charging or use in a grid connect inverter. Permanent magnet alternators have the advantage over conventional generators (shunt field or asynchronous/induction types) that need power to energise the generator's magnetic field. Permanent magnets function without external power. This ensures high efficiency in light winds, when energy is most needed. The winding of the alternator is usually either 'single phase' or 'three phase'. Single phase alternators are noisier than the three phase type. There are two types of magnets used in PMAs. Ferrite magnets are large and heavy – neodymium magnets are light but powerful. If weight is important, then neodymium magnets are preferable.

Electrical controls

The basic function of rectifying AC to DC is usually included, either in the machine or in a control panel with meters and fuses. However this may be a separate item with various options available. Wind turbine controllers will typically contain some sort of charge regulator based on a dump or diversion load, but often they are not very sophisticated.

In the case of grid-connected turbines, where the load is a special inverter, the wind turbine needs a controller that rectifies the current, meters and controls the turbine, and perhaps protects the inverter from excessive voltage.

Mechanical controls

These are needed on all but the very smallest machines, to protect them from damage in strong winds. The power in the wind can increase to extraordinarily high peaks during storms,

Bergey XL.1 turbine on a folding tower. The tail is in its furled position.

and it would be quite unrealistic to make the wind turbine strong enough to deliver this power to the user. To prevent dangerous overspeeding and/or burning out of the electrical parts, some means of limiting speed (rpm) is required.

The commonest solution is some sort of furling tail, which allows the rotor blades to swing sideways, away from the oncoming wind. In other machines the rotor itself tilts, ending up facing upward or downward. By facing away from the wind, a smaller frontal area is presented, and less energy is captured. The thrust forces on the tower are also reduced. The active force in these furling systems is the pressure of the wind itself on the rotor. When this pressure exceeds a certain limit, the machine yields and turns away, returning only when the wind has dropped again.

Blade pitch control is another strategy, which is more common in slightly larger machines (over 3m diameter). As rpm increases, centrifugal force is used to alter the pitch or setting angle of the blades, so that they stall. This spoils the efficiency and the speed is limited. Stalling of the blades is noisy, but normally only happens in high winds, when background noise levels are high. Pitch control is more difficult to engineer than furling tails or tilting systems, but it has two advantages: it responds more quickly to sudden changes in windspeed, giving smoother, more efficient performance, and speed (rpm) is limited regardless of windspeed. If the electrical system fails or becomes disconnected, some wind turbines can race like car engines at full throttle in neutral gear. Pitch control can prevent this sort of overspeed, which would otherwise occur in the case of 'loss of load'.

Very few small wind turbines have mechanical brakes. They can be used to 'park' the machine in case of problems or for erection of the tower. Others have 'brake switches' that short circuit the generator output. This prevents the rotor from starting up, but will not always stop it when running.

Orientation

The rotor can be the conventional horizontal axis (HAWT) or sometimes vertical axis (VAWT) see below. The VAWT turbines are at the end of Appendix 2. HAWTs can be conventionally upwind, or sometimes downwind of the tower.

'Upwind' is the normal position for the rotor in front of the tower, but there are some successful 'downwind' designs, where the blades rotate in the lee of the tower. This is a good strategy for rotors with very flexible blades, which might otherwise be pushed back until they strike the tower. Downwind turbines need no tail, but they sometimes have problems orienting to the wind direction at start-up.

Most machines are horizontal axis wind turbines (HAWTs). Another rotor orientation, which has always been popular among innovative designers and university engineering departments, is 'vertical axis wind turbine' (VAWT). In this orientation, the blades move like a roundabout, or petrol station sign. Vertical axis rotors are less efficient, and harder to start and control than horizontal axis rotors but the concept is very popular, perhaps due to its apparent simplicity. High speed vertical axis turbines usually suffer from early fatigue failures of the blades due to cyclical stresses in rotation.

No. of blades

This depends on the rated tip speed. Two-bladed rotors can run faster than three. This allows the manufacturer to fit a lighter, cheaper generator. Three-bladed rotors run more smoothly, especially in turbulent conditions. Six-bladed rotors are sometimes fitted to very small wind turbines. This is partly because multi-blades have more starting torque. (Starting can be a problem for very small wind turbines.) Another reason is that multi-blades are less prone to overspeed, and very small machines often have no speed controls.

Blade material

Glass reinforced polyester (GRP) or 'fibreglass' is the commonest choice of material. Carbon fibre is also used for reinforcement and there are many other plastics suitable for blade manufacture.

Lateral thrust

The maximum lateral thrust is useful information when designing a suitable tower. Rpm can be important in tower design, particularly in the case of two bladed rotors (that have pulsating thrust) to avoid resonant frequencies.

Tower top weight

The weight of the turbine (as installed on the tower top minus any shipping crates etc.) is interesting both in terms of selecting a tower and in terms of what it tells us about the way the turbine is made. Heavy wind turbines tend to be more expensive. They may well be more efficient but this cannot be assumed. However they do tend to last longer and withstand more hard knocks.

Conclusions

Stand-alone electricity supplies often simply evolve in a gradual, 'organic' fashion. Oil lamps are replaced or enhanced by a couple of 12 volt lights. A noisy diesel generator is kept running for a limited number of peak hours, and the house is supplied by an inverter at other times. Some good batteries arrive on the system as a welcome windfall from the local scrap merchant. And we always meant to get a bigger wind turbine...

This can be a very good way to collect the equipment you

need, especially if funds are limited at any one time and the house and family are expanding slowly, as they often do. Alternatively, the whole thing can be planned and installed at once. This will probably lead to a tidier system, but it also needs more courage and cash.

We hope that this book will help in the correct selection of equipment in either case. You will also need to collect information from a range of possible suppliers, check prices in *Exchange & Mart*, consult with your neighbours and the local authorities, pay regular visits to the scrap merchant (if you're a recycler), check the DTI web site for a windspeed estimate, consult with your tame electrical boffin, and try to explain what it all involves to the rest of the family. Try to visit someone who is already using a small wind system in similar circumstances. You may wish to go on a short residential course at the Centre for Alternative Technology and chew things over with the experts. Don't get so carried away that you opt for windpower in a situation where it is completely inappropriate, unsafe or a nuisance. There are other ways to be green, after all. But if the wind does turn out to be the greenest option for your electricity supply, then don't just be a dreamer: do it!

In summary:

- If you have no mains power available, assess your energy needs by listing the loads you need to run, estimating the power they use, and estimating the periods they will be used for. Will you need 'mains' voltage, and if so, what size and type of inverter?

- Assess your site's average windspeed, and see what size wind turbine might be appropriate. What height of tower would this need? Where exactly will you need to put it in order to be safe, avoid turbulence, meet planning requirements and keep cable costs to a minimum?

- Find out what wind turbines are available in this size, whether they have a good track record, and whether you can afford one. If not, you may wish to reassess your needs, or consider alternative supplies, perhaps to run in parallel with a smaller wind turbine. Cost the following items as well: tower; control electronics; cables; instruments (to keep an eye on things); battery; wiring, earthing and fuses; inverter. You may prefer to ask your supplier to design the system for you. Many will offer standard packages. The installation will go more smoothly if the installer and/or supplier are working with a familiar design.

- Apply for planning permission and/or grant, if appropriate. Always complete this process before ordering any equipment.

- If successful, place a firm order for the equipment you have chosen. Delivery can sometimes take several weeks. Meanwhile you can prepare the tower foundations and anchors, build the battery shed and do the necessary wiring. Your supplier will be delighted if all this is properly prepared when the wind turbine arrives (it usually is not).

- Hoist it up, release the brake and enjoy!

The case studies: the bottom line

As a round-up for the case studies, here are guesstimate prices in £s including VAT but not delivery/installation, for the components needed.

Case study	1	2	3	4
Wind turbine	650	1500	9000	3500
Tower	100	500	4000	2000
Cable	10	200	500	50
Battery	200	2000	3000	n/a
Shunt regulator	50	100	1000	n/a
Inverter	n/a	3000	3000	1500
Standby generator	n/a	4500	n/a	n/a
Totals:	1010	11800	20500	7050

Actual prices will depend greatly on details of site, and on the quality of equipment chosen.

Appendix 1: Glossary

AC 'alternating current' as produced by most generators, the mains, or an inverter. Can be 'rectified' into DC.

Alternator Type of electrical generator which produces AC.

Amps A measure of electric current in a cable.

Amphours From 'Ampere Hour' and not 'Amp per hour'. The measure of battery capacity. For example, a 200 amp-hour battery will give 20 amps for 10 hours, or 10 amps for 20 hours, in theory.

Back-up Another energy source, which can be used if wind is insufficient and the battery charge level is low.

Battery Batteries on stand-alone power systems are bigger and better built than car batteries. Energy must be stored during windy days for use in less windy weather later. The battery is a very expensive part of the system. It can be damaged by deep discharge and neglect.

Cables Copper wires contained in a plastic sheath. Thick cables are best for minimising losses on low-voltage systems. Armoured cables are best for outside use.

Circuit Breaker (MCB) Used in place of a fuse; this simply switches off if the current exceeds the safe value for the circuit.

Controller An electrical cabinet combining various control functions such as rectifier, charge regulator, meters and circuit protection.

Current The flow of electricity measured in amps. The amount of energy which is carried will also depend on the voltage.

DC 'direct current' as used for charging batteries. Batteries also supply DC output. This can be used in lighting or converted to AC by an inverter.

Deep cycle When most or all of the energy stored in a battery is used before being recharged. (Car batteries do not like this treatment.)

Dump load A small heater, which is used to 'dump' surplus energy. The charge regulator diverts unwanted current to it automatically.

Energy The ability to do work, provide light, heat and switch things on. In its most popular form, that of electricity, energy is measured in units called kilowatt hours (kWh).

Fuse A safety device that melts when overloaded, cutting off the supply current to a faulty circuit. Usually it is made from a piece of low-melting-point wire.

Heating Electric heating uses large amounts of energy. Wind-powered heating systems need large turbines. Direct heating with a wind turbine is simple to install but much less rewarding than producing electricity. Electrical energy can be converted into three times as much heat energy with a heat pump.

Inverter A complex device for converting DC to AC for mains voltage loads.

Load Anything that uses electricity, for example a light or a radio.

Losses Energy from the wind needs to be moved around, stored and converted by the system. At each stage some of it is lost, usually as heat.

Mains or grid power Supplied by the national grid, is 230 volt AC power, as used by most electricity consumers in this country.

Power The rate of delivery of energy. Energy per hour. Measured in watts (W) or kilowatts (kW). 1 kW = 1,000 W.

Rated The value of a parameter such as windspeed or power that has been used for designing some equipment. For instance, if the 'rated voltage' of a light bulb is 12 volts, then it will give best overall performance at this voltage.

Rectifier Passive semiconductor device which converts AC to DC.

Regulator Electronic device that controls voltage by reducing the current charging the battery. The battery will charge best if the voltage is limited to a maximum value.

Rotor blades The 'propeller', 'sails 'or 'wings' of a wind turbine. Their job is to take energy from the wind and turn the generator.

Shunt regulator An electronic device for controlling battery charge rate. When the battery is full, the charge rate is reduced by diverting current through a dump load.

Site The position where the wind turbine is used. The wind speed at the site is the most important factor in the whole system.

Speed Windspeed is measured in metres per second (m/s). 10m/s = 22mph.

Tower Name for whatever is used to support the wind turbine. Often this will be a simple tubular mast, guyed with wires.

Turnkey A type of system where all installation and management problems are dealt with by the supplier so it 'just works'. Clearly this is a high-cost option.

Turbulence Random chaotic movement of air containing revolving masses called vortices. Turbulence is always present to some degree. It interferes with successful energy capture by wind turbines.

Voltage The electrical 'pressure difference' between two wires. All components connected to any particular supply should have the same nominal voltage rating. The advantage of higher voltage systems is that more power can be carried from A to B using less current, so thinner cable can be used. Other components, such as inverters, wind turbines, etc, will remain the same size regardless of voltage (for a given power rating). The battery will have more, smaller cells in series to store the same energy. If the battery is disconnected then the wind turbine will usually produce excessive voltage and damage the other components very quickly.

Voltage drop Loss of voltage and power due to resistance of the wire. Loss increases as the length of the cable increases, and decreases with its thickness.

Watts A measure of power: the rate of delivery of energy at any one instant. One kilowatt (kW) is 1,000 watts (W).

Wind turbine Machine that converts the energy of moving air into electricity.

Appendix 2: Market survey

Machines are listed by rotor diameter. VAWT machines are listed at the end.

Model	Rutland 503	A2	A4 (&A4F)	Rutland 913
Manufacturer	Marlec	LVM	LVM	Marlec
Nationality	UK	UK	UK	UK
Price £ (inc. 17.5% vat)	£279.95	£376.00	£623 (A4F is £750)	£455.99
Included in price	-	-	-	-
Rotor diameter	**0.51m**	**0.58m**	**0.87m**	**0.91m**
Energy at 5m/s site	0.9 kWh/wk	-	-	4.2 kWh/wk
Cut-in windspeed	3.0m/s	3.0m/s	3.0m/s	3.0m/s
Power at 10m/s	25W	18W	70W	72W
Rated windspeed	10.0m/s	11.0m/s	10.0m/s	9.5m/s
Rated power	25W	20W	72W	90W
Peak power	80W	-	-	300W
Rated rpm	900rpm	-	-	700rpm
Application	Battery charging	Battery charging	Battery charging	Battery charging
Voltages	12V	12/24V	12/24V	12/24V
Generator type	3-ph PMA ferrite	pm alternator	pm alternator	3-ph PMA ferrite
Electrical controls	Charge regulators	Charge regulators	Charge regulators	Charge regulators
Mechanical controls	No protection	None	'F' type have	No protection
Orientation	upwind HAWT	upwind HAWT	upwind HAWT	upwind HAWT
No. of blades	6	5	6	6
Blade material	Glass reinforced nylon	Glass filled polypropylene	Glass filled polypropylene	Glass reinforced nylon
Lateral thrust	9kg	-	9kg	4 kg
Tower top weight	4kg	5kg	9kg	1 kg

Model	Rutland FM910-3	Hawk/Pacific	Stealthgen/D400	AIR X	A6 (&A6F)
Manufacturer	Marlec	Ampair	Eclectic energy	Southwest Windpower	LVM
Nationality	UK	UK	UK	USA	UK
Price £ (inc. 17.5% vat)	£539.95	£630.00	£875.00	£581.63	£940 (A6F is £1003)
Included in price	-	-	-	Internal regulator MPPT	-
Rotor diameter	0.91m	0.92m	1.1m	1.2m	1.22m
Energy at 5m/s site	-	-	7.0 kWh/wk	7.0 kWh/wk	-
Cut-in windspeed	3.0m/s	3.0m/s	2.6m/s	3.6 m/s	3.0m/s
Power at 10m/s	72W	55W	210W	200W	120W
Rated windspeed	10.0m/s	20.0m/s	16.5m/s	12.5 m/s	10.0m/s
Rated power	72W	100W	400W	400W	120W
Peak power	200W	100W	500W	550W	120W
Rated rpm	800rpm	-	1200 rpm	-	-
Application	Battery charging	Battery charging	Battery & gridlink	Battery charging	Battery charging
Voltages	12/24V	12/24V	12/24/48/150V	12/24V	12/24V
Generator type	3-ph PMA ferrite	2-ph PMA ferrite	3-ph PMA ferrite	3-ph PMA neo	pm alternator
Electrical controls	Charge regulators	Series regulator	Stall regulation	Internal regulator MPPT	Charge regulators
Mechanical controls	Furling tail	None required	-	Stall	'F' type have
Orientation	upwind HAWT	upwind HAWT	upwind HAWT	upwind HAWT	upwind HAWT
No. of blades	6	6	5	3	6
Blade material	Glass reinforced nylon	Glass filled polypropylene	Glass filled nylon	Carbon fibre	Glass filled polypropylene
Lateral thrust	13kg	24kg	15kg	-	-
Tower top weight	13kg	13kg	15kg	6kg	13kg

Model	Inclin 250	Windsave	Airdolphin	Rutland FM 1803	Inclin 600
Manufacturer	Bornay	Windsave	Zephir	Marlec	Bornay
Nationality	Spain	UK	Japan	UK	Spain
Price £ (inc. 17.5% vat)	£1,845.00	£1,874.13	£2,560.00	£1,575.95	£2,338.00
Included in price	Regulator	Fully installed	Fully installed	-	Regulator
Rotor diameter	1.4m	1.75m	1.80m	1.87m	2.0m
Energy at 5m/s site	-	-	24.0 kWh/wk	15.0 kWh/wk	-
Cut-in windspeed	3.0m/s	4.0m/s	2.5m/s	2.0m/s	3.5m/s
Power at 10m/s	200W	530W	620W	240W	-
Rated windspeed	11.0m/s	12.0m/s	12.5m/s	15.0m/s	11.0m/s
Rated power	250W	1000W	1000W	720W	600W
Peak power	-	1100W	3200W	-	-
Rated rpm	-	800 rpm	1250 rpm	870rpm	-
Application	Battery charging	Gridlink	Battery & gridlink	Battery charging	Battery charging
Voltages	12/24V	-	25V	12/24V	12/24/48V
Generator type	3-ph PMA ferrite	Single phase PMA	3-ph PMA neo	3-ph PMA ferrite	3-ph PMA ferrite
Electrical controls	Charge regulators	Gridlink inverter	Internal regulator MPPT	Charge regulators,	Charge regulators
Mechanical controls	Tilt-back governor	Furling tail with spring	Stall	Furling tail	Tilt-back governor
Orientation	upwind HAWT	upwind HAWT	upwind HAWT	upwind HAWT	upwind HAWT
No. of blades	2	3	3	3	2
Blade material	Nylon	Glass reinforced polyamide	Carbon fibre	Foam cored GRP	Carbon fibre
Lateral thrust	-	-	-	56kg	-
Tower top weight	25kg	25kg	17.5kg	39kg	38kg

Model	Whisper 100	Swift	Fortis Espada	Navitron 200W	BWC XL 1
Manufacturer	Southwest Windpower	Renewable Energy Devices	Fortis	China	Bergey Windpower
Nationality	USA	UK	NL		USA
Price £ (inc. 17.5% vat)	£1,515.75	£4,112.50	£6,932.50	£299.00	£2,000.00
Included in price	Charge regulators	Controller	Full system package	Controller & inverter	Controller
Rotor diameter	**2.1m**	**2.1m**	**2.2m**	**2.2m**	**2.5m**
Energy at 5m/s site	20.0 kWh/wk	56.0 kWh/wk	–	–	36.0 kWh/wk
Cut-in windspeed	3.4m/s	2.3m/s	3.0m/s	3.0m/s	2.5m/s
Power at 10m/s	500W	970W	480W	260W	900W
Rated windspeed	12.5m/s	12.5m/s	17.0m/s	6.0m/s	11.0m/s
Rated power	900W	1500W	800W	200W	1000W
Peak power	900W	–	800W	300W	1300W
Rated rpm	–	600 rpm	1000 rpm	450 rpm	490rpm
Application	Battery charging	Gridlink & heat	Battery & gridlink	Battery & gridlink	Battery charging
Voltages	12/24/36/48V	60V	12/24VDC	12/24V	12V ?
Generator type	3-ph PMA ferrite	pm alternator	pm alternator	3-ph PMA neo	3-ph PMA neo
Electrical controls	Charge regulators	MPPT controller & inverter	Charge regulators	Charge controller/inverter	Charge regulators
Mechanical controls	Angle governor	Furling tail	Furling tail	Furling tail	Furling tail
Orientation	upwind HAWT	upwind HAWT	upwind HAWT	upwind HAWT	upwind HAWT
No. of blades	3	5	2	3	3
Blade material	Carbon fibre polypropylene	Carbon fibre	GRP	GRP	Extruded GRP ?
Lateral thrust	90kg	260kg	–	–	107kg
Tower top weight	21kg	40kg	52kg	20kg	38kg

Model	Navitron 300W	WT 600	Navitron 500W	Powerbreeze A800	Inclin 1500
Manufacturer	China	Proven Energy	China	Anhua	Bornay
Nationality	China	Scotland, UK	China	China	Spain
Price £ (inc. 17.5% vat)	£349.00	£2,167.88	£525.00	£918.00	£3,407.50
Included in price	Controller & inverter	-	Controller & inverter	Charge regulators	Regulator
Rotor diameter	2.5m	2.6m	2.7m	2.8m	2.9m
Energy at 5m/s site	-	24.0 kWh/wk	-	20kWh/wk@4m/s	-
Cut-in windspeed	3.0m/s	2.5m/s	3.0m/s	4.0m/s	3.5m/s
Power at 10m/s	370W	600W	550W	650W	1250W
Rated windspeed	7.0m/s	10.0m/s	8.0m/s	8.0m/s	12.0m/s
Rated power	300W	600W	500W	500W	1500W
Peak power	400W	700W	700W	900W	1800W
Rated rpm	400 rpm	500rpm	400 rpm	-	-
Application	Battery & gridlink	Battery & gridlink	Battery & gridlink	Battery & gridlink	Battery & gridlink
Voltages	12/24V	12/24/48V	24/36V	24/36V	24/48V
Generator type	3-ph PMA neo	3-ph PMA ferrite	3-ph PMA neo	pm alternator	3-ph PMA neo
Electrical controls	Charge controller/inverter	Charge regulators	Charge controller/inverter	Charge regulators	Charge regulators
Mechanical controls	Furling tail	Centrifugal blade pitch	Furling tail	Furling tail	Tilt-back governor
Orientation	upwind HAWT	downwind HAWT	upwind HAWT	upwind HAWT	upwind HAWT
No. of blades	3	3	3	3	2
Blade material	GRP	Polypropylene	GRP	Foam cored GRP	Carbon fibre
Lateral thrust	-	250kg	-	-	400kg
Tower top weight	25kg	75kg	30kg	90kg	42kg

Model	Whisper 200	Navitron 1kW	Fortis Passat	Powerbreeze B1500	WT 2500
Manufacturer	Southwest Windpower		Fortis	Anhua	Proven Energy
Nationality	USA	China	NL	China	Scotland, UK
Price £ (inc. 17.5% vat)	£1,833.00	£725.00	£9,752.50	£1,404.00	£4,294.63
Included in price	Charge regulators	Controller & inverter	Full systempackage	Charge regulators	-
Rotor diameter	**3.0m**	**3.1m**	**3.1m**	**3.2m**	**3.4m**
Energy at 5m/s site	35.0 kWh/wk	-	?	30kWh/wk@4m/s	70.0 kWh/wk
Cut-in windspeed	3.1m/s	3.0m/s	3.2m/s	3.0m/s	2.5m/s
Power at 10m/s	900W	1000W	720W	1200W	1800W
Rated windspeed	11.6m/s	9.0m/s	15.0m/s	9.0m/s	12.0m/s
Rated power	1000W	1000W	1400W	1000W	2500W
Peak power	1000W	1500W	1400W	1500W	2900W
Rated rpm	-	400 rpm	775 rpm	-	300rpm
Application	Battery & gridlink	Battery charging	Battery & gridlink	Battery & gridlink	Battery, heat & gridlink
Voltages	12/24/36/48V	48V	-	48/240V	24/48/120V
Generator type	3-ph PMA ferrite	3-ph PMA neo	pm alternator	pm alternator	3-ph PMA ferrite
Electrical controls	Charge regulators	Charge controller/inverter	Charge regulators	Charge regulators	Charge regulators
Mechanical controls	Angle governor	Furling tail	Furling tail	Furling tail	Blade pitch and brake
Orientation	upwind HAWT	upwind HAWT	upwind HAWT	upwind HAWT	downwind HAWT
No. of blades	3	3	3	3	3
Blade material	Carbon fibre polypropylene	GRP	GRP	Foam cored GRP	Polypropylene
Lateral thrust	112kg	-	-	-	500kg
Tower top weight	30kg	42kg	75kg	120kg	190kg

Model	Navitron 2kW	Inclin 3000	Whisper 175	Fortis Montana	Powerbreeze C5000
Manufacturer	China	Bornay	Southwest Windpower	Fortis	Anhua
Nationality	China	Spain	USA	NL	China
Price £ (inc. 17.5% vat)	£1,600.00	£3,491.00	£ 4,641.25	£18,565.00	£4,431.00
Included in price	Controller & inverter	Regulator	Charge regulators	Full systempackage	Charge regulators
Rotor diameter	**3.7m**	**4.0m**	**4.3m**	**5.0m**	**5.0m**
Energy at 5m/s site	-	-	95.0 kWh/wk	-	63kWh/day@4m/s
Cut-in windspeed	3.0m/s	3.5m/s	3.0m/s	2.0m/s	3.0m/s
Power at 10m/s	2400W	2600W	2500W	2700W	3500W
Rated windspeed	9.0m/s	12.0m/s	12.0m/s	14.0m/s	10.0m/s
Rated power	2000W	3000W	3200W	5000W	3500W
Peak power	2600W	3500W	3200W	5800W	5500W
Rated rpm	400 rpm	-	-	450 rpm	-
Application	Battery & gridlink	Battery & gridlink	Battery & gridlink	Battery & gridlink	Battery & gridlink
Voltages	220V ?	24/48V battery & grid connect	24/48V	?	240/500V
Generator type	3-ph PMA neo	3-ph PMA neo	3-ph PMA ferrite	pm alternator	pm alternator
Electrical controls	Charge controller/inverter	Charge regulators	Charge regulators	Charge regulators	Charge regulators
Mechanical controls	Furling tail or auto program	Tilt-back governor	Angle governor	Furling tail	Furling tail
Orientation	upwind HAWT	upwind HAWT	upwind HAWT	upwind HAWT	upwind HAWT
No. of blades	3	2	2	3	3
Blade material	GRP	Carbon fibre	Foam cored GRP	Fibreglass epoxy	Foam cored GRP
Lateral thrust	-	750kg	300kg	-	-
Tower top weight	52kg	125kg	82kg	200kg	300kg

Model	Tupilo	ATS-1	WT 6000	Sirocco	Navitron 5kW
Manufacturer	WES	Iskra	Proven Energy	Eoltec	China
Nationality	NL	UK	Scotland, UK	France	China
Price £ (inc. 17.5% vat)		£8,812.50	£9,123.88	£16,450.00	£4,690.00
Included in price		-	-	Inverter	Controller & inverter
Rotor diameter	**5.0m**	**5.4m**	**5.5m**	**5.6m**	**6.0m**
Energy at 5m/s site	120.0 kWh/wk	170.0 kWh/wk	220.0 kWh/wk	210.0 kWh/wk	210.0 kWh/wk
Cut-in windspeed	3 m/s (powered)	3.0 m/s	2.5 m/s	2.7 m/s	3.0 m/s
Power at 10m/s	2500W	4400W	5000W	5000W	4000W
Rated windspeed	10.0 m/s	12.0 m/s	12.0 m/s	11.5 m/s	11.0 m/s
Rated power	2500W	5000W	6000W	6000W	5000W
Peak power	2600W	5000W	6500W	6000W	8000W
Rated rpm	140 rpm	200 rpm	200rpm	245 rpm	200 rpm
Application	Gridlink	Battery & gridlink	Battery, heat & gridlink	Battery & gridlink	Battery & gridlink
Voltages	400VAC	380VDC	48/120/240V (DC)	-	240V
Generator type	pm alternator	3-ph PMA neo	3-ph PMA ferrite	3-ph PMA neo	3-ph PMA neo
Electrical controls	Variable speed IGBT converter	Gridlink inverter	Charge regulators	Gridlink inverter	Charge controller/inverter
Mechanical controls	Active yawing	Passive blade pitching	Blade pitch and brake	Centrifugal blade pitch	Auto program
Orientation	upwind HAWT	upwind HAWT	downwind HAWT	upwind HAWT	upwind HAWT
No. of blades	3	3	3	2	3
Blade material	GRP	GRP	Polypropylene	epoxy	GRP
Lateral thrust	-	660kg	-	-	-
Tower top weight	940kg	280kg	450kg	202kg	1253kg

Model	BWC Exel	Powerbreeze D9500	Navitron 10kW	Jacobs 29-20	Powerbreeze E20000
Manufacturer	Bergey Windpower	Anhua		Wind Turbine Industries	Anhua
Nationality	USA	China	China	USA	China
Price £ (inc. 17.5% vat)	£32,900.00	£11,488.00	£8,250.00	£35,250.00	£16,348.00
Included in price	Fully installed	Charge regulators	Controller & inverter	Fully installed	Charge regulators
Rotor diameter	**7.0m**	**7.0m**	**8.0m**	**9.4m**	**10.0m**
Energy at 5m/s site	174.0 kWh/wk	210.0 kWh/wk	-	-	200.0 kWh/wk
Cut-in windspeed	3.4m/s	3.0m/s	3.0m/s	3.6m/s	3.0m/s
Power at 10m/s	6500W	7500W	10000W	13000W	15000W
Rated windspeed	16.0m/s	10.0m/s	10.0m/s	11.6m/s	10.0m/s
Rated power	10000W	7500W	10000W	20000W	15000W
Peak power	-	9500W	14000W	-	21000W
Rated rpm	310rpm	-	200 rpm	175rpm	100 rpm
Application	Battery (7.5kW) & gridlink	Battery & gridlink	Battery & gridlink	Gridlink	Battery & gridlink
Voltages	48/120V	240/500V	240V	-	500V
Generator type	3-ph PMA ferrite	pm alternator	3-ph PMA neo	Geared 3-ph Brushless synchronous	pm alternator
Electrical controls	Charge regulators	Charge regulators	Charge controller/inverter	Gridlink inverter	Charge regulators
Mechanical controls	Furling tail	Furling tail	Auto program	Blade pitch, brake & furling tail	Furling tail
Orientation	upwind HAWT	upwind HAWT	upwind HAWT	upwind HAWT	upwind HAWT
No. of blades	3	3	3	3	3
Blade material	Extruded GRP	Foam cored GRP	GRP	Fibreglass	Foam cored GRP
Lateral thrust	893kg	-	-	-	-
Tower top weight	463kg	655kg	1590kg	1100kg	120kg

Model	Westwind 20kW	Gazelle	Navitron 20kW
Manufacturer	Westwind	GazelleWind Turbines Ltd.	
Nationality	Australia	UK	China
Price £ (inc. 17.5% vat)	£47,000.00	£85,775.00	£14,500.00
Included in price	Fully installed	Fully installed	Controller & inverter
Rotor diameter	**10.4m**	**11m**	**12.0m**
Energy at 5m/s site	-	1150kWh @ 6.5m/s	-
Cut-in windspeed	3.0m/s	4.0m/s	3.0m/s
Power at 10m/s	12500W	-	14000W
Rated windspeed	14.0m/s	13.5m/s	12.0m/s
Rated power	20000W	20000W	20000W
Peak power	-	-	25000W
Rated rpm	-	106rpm	160 rpm
Application	Battery, heat & gridlink	Gridlink	Battery & gridlink
Voltages	240V	400V 3 phase	420V
Generator type	3-ph PMA neo	Geared 4 pole induction	3-ph PMA neo
Electrical controls	Shunt regulator	G59 supervision relay	Charge controller/inverter
Mechanical controls	Rotor pitch	Passive stall & two brakes	Auto program
Orientation	upwind HAWT	downwind HAWT	upwind HAWT
No. of blades	3	3	3
Blade material	GRP	Carbon fibre epoxy	GRP
Lateral thrust	-	1086kg	-
Tower top weight	750kg	1000kg	1850kg

Model	WRE.007	WRE.030	WRE.060
Manufacturer	Ropatec	Ropatec	Ropatec
Nationality	Italy	Italy	Italy
Price £ (inc. 17.5% vat)	£4,112.50	£10,340.00	£16,450.00
Included in price	Battery charger	Full system & PV	Full gridlink system
Rotor diameter	**1.5m(x1.5 high)**	**3.3 (x2.2m high)**	**3.3(x4.4 high)**
Energy at 5m/s site	7.0 kWh/wk	30.0 kWh/wk	60.0 kWh/wk
Cut-in windspeed	3.0m/s	2.0m/s	2.0m/s
Power at 10m/s	280W	1000W	2000W
Rated windspeed	14.0m/s	14.0m/s	14.0m/s
Rated power	750W	2500W	5000W
Peak power	–	5000W	–
Rated rpm	340 rpm	120 rpm	120 rpm
Application	Battery, heat & gridlink	Battery, heat & gridlink	Battery, heat & gridlink
Voltages	120VAC	220VAC	–
Generator type	pm alternator	pm alternator	pm alternator
Electrical controls	Chargers & gridlink	Chargers & gridlink	Chargers & gridlink
Mechanical controls	Aerodynamically auto regulated	Aerodynamically auto regulated	Aerodynamically auto regulated
Orientation	VAWT	VAWT	VAWT
No. of blades	3	2	2
Blade material	Foam-backed aluminium	Foam-backed aluminium	Foam-backed aluminium
Lateral thrust	–	–	–
Tower top weight	160kg	500kg	750kg

Appendix 3: Useful equations

The following equations can be used for calculations, or included in computer spreadsheets, to help with successful design of systems.

A	Cross-sectional area of copper wire in cable (in square millimetres)
CP	Power coefficient (measure of efficiency – cannot exceed 0.6 and should exceed 0.1)
D	Rotor diameter (metres)
DP	Power loss (watts)
DV	Volt drop (volts)
E	Energy (kWh)
I	Electric current (amps)
L	Length of a twin copper cable one way (metres)
P	Power (watts)
RPM	Rotational speed (rpm)
T	Time (hours)
V	System voltage (volts)
VT	Tip speed (m/s)
VW	Windspeed (m/s)
x	multiplication symbol
/	divide by what follows

Cables: Volt drop   DV = L x I/(28 x A)   Where I = P/V

Power loss   DP = DV x I = L x I2/(30 x A)

For example if the turbine produces 1000 watts and the system voltage is 24, then we can say that the current I = P/V = 1000/24 = 42 amps

Now if the length of the cable is 50 metres and the wire size is 25 sqmm, then the volt drop DV = L x I/(28 x A) = 50 x 42/(28 x 25)= 3 volts

And power loss = 3 x 24 = 72 watts.

Acceptable loss will depend on the relative cost of the system and the cable, but we usually try to keep it below 10%.

Energy: E = P x T/1000 = V x I x T/1000

= V x amp-hours/1000

For example a 20 watt lamp over a 24 hour period will use E = P x T/1000 = 20 x 24 /1000 = 0.48 kWh or half a unit of electricity

If we have a 12 volt, 100 amp-hour battery then the energy it contains is

E = V x amp-hours/1000 = 12 x 100 / 1000 = 1.2 kWh

But it is not advisable to completely drain the battery so we would normally only plan to use about half of this energy before recharging it.

Tip speed: VT = RPM x D/19.1

For example a 5 metre diameter turbine running at 300 rpm will have a tip speed VT = RPM x D/19.1 = 300 x 5/19.1 = 78 m/s. This is quite fast. Tip speeds over 80 m/s tend to cause problems with noise and erosion of the blades.

Power coeff: CP = P/(0.48 x D2 x VW3)

The power coefficient is a measure of the 'efficiency' of the wind turbine at converting wind energy. We would like this to be high, but it is worth checking whether the claimed efficiency is physically possible. A very basic theory of wind turbines (attributed to Betz) proves that it is impossible to convert more than 59.3% of the energy that passes through the rotor. This is because the process of slowing the wind down also causes it to divert away from the blade area and so it is impossible to capture all the energy. In practice a power coefficient of 40% is ambitious but possible.

For example Bornay claim that their 2.9 metre turbine can produce 600 watts in a 6m/s wind.

CP = P/(0.48 x D2 x VW3)) = 600/(0.48 x 2.9 x 2.9 x 6 x 6 x 6)
= 0.69 or 69%

This output is physically impossible, so we should take their claims with a pinch of salt.

For those who wish to study windspeed distributions and turbine power curves and use them to derive estimates of energy production, there is a nicely made spreadsheet on the web site for Bergey Windpower www.bergey.com. Search the technical section for a spreadsheet they call 'windCAD'. Playing with spreadsheets is fun, but remember the rule 'garbage in, garbage out'. Manufacturers' power curves are rarely verified by any independent tests.

Appendix 4: Web links

The author's web page http://www.scoraigwind.co.uk offers a lot of information in rather a chaotic format. The main emphasis is on building one's own wind turbine.

The Danish wind energy web page http://www.windpower.org has a lot of good basic information about wind turbines.

Home Power Magazine have a web site http://www.homepowercom with useful case studies and reviews of the latest products for domestic renewable energy systems. You can download the magazine for free from the site or take out a subscription from http://www.windandsun.co.uk

The British Wind Energy Association web page http://www.bwea.com is useful for keeping abreast of the latest UK news. It has a link for the DTI website where mean windspeed estimates can be found from map references. The actual DTI url tends to change from time to time.

Bergey Windpower http://www.bergey.com offer a useful spreadsheet (windCAD under 'technical stuff') for calculating energy production on different sites. You can modify the spreadsheet by changing the power curve to any other machine that interests you.

✳

For grants in the UK, go to
http://www.lowcarbonbuildings.org.uk
or http://www.est.org.uk run by the Energy Savings Trust.
They also have lists of approved turbines and installers on
these sites.

0800 512012